MARRIAGE ON THE ROCK

A GUIDE FOR DISCOVERING
GOD'S DESIGN FOR YOUR DREAM MARRIAGE

COUPLE'S WORKBOOK

JIMMY EVANS

Marriage on the Rock Couple's Workbook

Based on the *Marriage on the Rock* seminar by Jimmy Evans, this couple's guide is designed as a companion for the DVD or CD series. *Marriage on the Rock* is available on book, DVD, CD, and workbooks for couples and small groups.

MarriageToday™
P.O. Box 59888
Dallas, Texas 75229
1-800-380-6330
marriagetoday.com

Written by Phillip Chapman.

Layout by Morgan G. Farris.

A GUIDE FOR DISCOVERING
GOD'S DESIGN FOR YOUR DREAM MARRIAGE

COUPLE'S WORKBOOK

TABLE OF CONTENTS

ACKNOWLEDGEMENTS

Jimmy and Karen Evans

I would like to acknowledge the many people who have contributed to the publication of the *Marriage on the Rock Couple's Guide.*

Thank you to Phillip Chapman, who wrote this workbook based on my *Marriage on the Rock* series. He designed this guide to help couples discuss and apply these teachings so they have a lasting impact for years to come.

Thanks to our incredible MarriageToday™ team who work tirelessly to produce our TV show, plan events, create resources and equip churches. Marriages around the world are forever changed due to their efforts for God's glory.

To the Board of Directors of MarriageToday™, thank you. Words cannot express the gratitude I feel for your unwavering support and commitment to me and the call of God upon my life. Without your support this book would not have been possible.

Thank you to the elders, staff and congregation of Trinity Fellowship Church in Amarillo, Texas, for supporting us and allowing us to fulfill our ministry to marriages. We are grateful for the love and support we continually receive from each of you.

And most importantly, thank you Karen. You have stood by me and loved me for more than forty years. Even when I didn't believe it was possible, you had faith in us. Because of your prayers, we have built our *Marriage on the Rock.*

May God bless you,

Jimmy Evans

ABOUT JIMMY EVANS

Jimmy Evans is Founder and CEO of MarriageToday™, a ministry that is devoted to helping couples thrive in strong and fulfilling marriages and families. Jimmy and his wife, Karen, co-host *MarriageToday™ with Jimmy & Karen*, a nationally syndicated television program which is broadcast daily into over 110 million homes in America and more than 200 countries worldwide.

Jimmy has served as the senior leader of Trinity Fellowship in Amarillo, Texas, for over 30 years. Jimmy has authored more than ten books, among which are his popular works, *Marriage on the Rock, Freedom From Your Past, Seven Secrets of Successful Families, Ten Steps Toward Christ, Lifelong Love Affair,* and his newest book, *When Life Hurts*.

Jimmy and Karen have been married over 40 years and have two married children and five grandchildren.

INTRODUCTION

Welcome to the excitement and blessing that comes from participating in a *Marriage on the Rock* study with your spouse.

This couple's workbook is based on the *Marriage on the Rock* seminar and is designed as a companion for Jimmy Evans' DVD or CD series. This resource has helped thousands of couples recapture the intimacy and passion they believed was long removed from their marriage.

Through the next ten sessions, you will embark on a journey that will dramatically increase the intimacy in your relationship. This workbook will provide you with practical, biblically-based guidelines, insightful discussions and life-changing applications.

As you prepare for the first session, we want to encourage you in three areas:

   • **First, be committed.** If you and your spouse are committed to God first and then to each other, your marriage can survive anything and become the marriage of your dreams.

   • **Second, be bold.** Some of the discussion questions may challenge you to talk about important issues. It's normal to feel some resistance when you've been hurt or disappointed. However, it's important to let your spouse know what's really going on in your heart and mind.

   • **Third, focus on what you can do.** Some discussion questions may present an opportunity to be critical of your spouse. There will be times when you can lovingly say how you feel about important issues. But the key to achieving intimacy is a willingness to focus on what you can do yourself.

The bottom line is that none of us have a perfect marriage. The joy of marriage is learning how to become one and growing together with your spouse as God intended.

USING THIS WORKBOOK AS A COUPLE

Each session of your workbook will include the following sections.

DVD TEACHING WITH JIMMY EVANS

The *Marriage on the Rock* DVD series includes ten videos from Jimmy Evans' seminar. Each video is approximately 40-45 minutes in length. The sessions directly correspond with the content in this couple's guide.

As you watch each message, you can follow along with the teaching outline in your workbook.

TALK IT OUT: COUPLE HOME ACTIVITY

This section of your workbook features fill-in-the blank and multiple choice questions to help you review key themes from the DVD teaching.

WALK IT OUT: COUPLE HOME DISCUSSION

Before you move on to the next session, you and your spouse should discuss the "Walk It Out" questions in order to fully apply Jimmy's teaching to your marriage. You will want to find a time that is good for both of you to talk so that you can give each other your best.

Some questions will immediately draw you closer to your spouse. Other questions may even bring some tension or frustration to the surface. This is normal. When needed, take a break and revisit the questions later at an agreed upon time.

Be committed to the process of working through this guide. Trust that the end result will be that you and your spouse will have a thriving marriage greater than you ever thought possible.

USING THIS WORKBOOK AS A GROUP

The *Marriage on the Rock Couple's Workbook* can also be used in a group or classroom environment.

Some large groups like to show the DVD teaching and then let the truth of Jimmy's message speak to each spouse individually. In this case, you can discuss the "Talk It Out" and "Walk It Out" sections at home before the class meets again.

If you are facilitating a class in a large group environment, consider completing the "Talk It Out" section of the workbook directly after the teaching with your large group. This will be a fun way to review the material before the couples dismiss. They can then complete the "Walk It Out" discussion with each other before the class meets again.

However you use the *Marriage on the Rock Couple's Workbook*, we pray that this resource will strengthen your marriage for many years to come.

God bless you as you begin this journey together.

SESSION ONE

THE MOST IMPORTANT ISSUE IN MARRIAGE

Are you depending on God or your spouse to meet your deepest needs?

It's a fact of life, people are going to let us down and frustrate us. Hurts from our parents, a dating relationship, or even our spouse can leave us feeling rejected and heartbroken. Life's not like a movie. We have to work at our happily ever after.

Marriage was created by God as a spiritual union, not simply a piece of paper. God's desire is to be an integral part of your relationship. In order to find fulfillment and total satisfaction, God needs to be at the center of your life and your marriage.

Today you'll discover the most important issue that will determine if you are going to have the marriage of your dreams…

DVD TEACHING WITH JIMMY EVANS

Below is an outline of today's teaching. Feel free to take additional notes in the space provided as you listen to Jimmy share biblical truths on having a successful marriage.

THE MOST IMPORTANT ISSUE
IN MARRIAGE

Related Scriptures: *John 4:5-24, Romans 8:35-39, 1 John 4:18, Psalm 139, Revelation 2:17, Psalm 91, Jeremiah 29:11-14, Galatians 5:22-23*

The Story of the Samaritan Woman at the Well

a) Jesus has compassion for those who are struggling or have failed in marriage.

b) Marriage was created by God and is only successful when it honors His plan and includes His presence.

c) The most important issue in marriage is whether you have a personal relationship with God through Jesus Christ.

Our Four Deepest Needs

a) Acceptance – "I am loved and accepted for who I am." (Romans 8:35-39)

Most people love us based on what they don't know. God is the only one who knows your every thought and will always love you no matter what.

b) Identity – "I am special, unique and significant." (Psalm 139)

God planned every day of your life before you were born. He is the only one who knows why you were created.

When we get to heaven, God is going to give us a white stone with our real name on it. No one else knows our real name. (Revelation 2:17)

c) Security – "I am safe and secure from harm." (Psalm 91)

When you understand God's security it doesn't matter what is going on around you, because God's security is in you.

d) Purpose – "I have a significant purpose and there is a reason for my life." (Jeremiah 29:11-14)

God's purpose for your life will fulfill the desires of your heart. He won't lead you to do something that He hasn't prepared you to do.

The Danger of Trusting Other People

a) The Principle of Transference - If we don't trust Jesus to meet our deepest needs, we will automatically transfer the expectation of those needs to those closest to us, especially our spouse.

b) When you depend on others to meet your deepest needs:

1) You will never be fulfilled.

2) You will become discouraged and cynical.

3) You will become bitter toward people and reject them for not meeting your expectations.

c) When you trust something or someone to meet your deepest needs:

1) Your inner security is dependant upon something or someone you cannot predict or control.

2) Your ability to give is dependant upon your ability to get from others.

3) Your life is filled with an atmosphere of disappointment and frustration.

4) Your unrealistic expectations of others create a negative atmosphere of tension in your relationship.

d) When you have a problem, where do you go first?

1) We all have problems, especially relational problems that only God can solve.

2) God will not only heal you, but He will fill you with the fruits of the spirit: love, joy, peace, patience, kindness, goodness, faithfulness, gentleness and self-control. (Galatians 5:22-23)

3) When you depend on God, He will help change all the relationships in your life.

e) How to experience a personal relationship with Jesus:

1) Remember that Jesus is a gift of grace from God.

2) Ask Him for what you need.

3) Have faith in God's love and faithfulness.

ADDITIONAL NOTES FROM TODAY'S TEACHING

TALK IT OUT:
COUPLE HOME ACTIVITY

Review the highlights from the video session of *Marriage on the Rock* with your spouse. Look over your outline on the previous pages if needed and answer the following questions.

What are the three key points from the meeting of Jesus and the woman at the well? Put a check beside those three statements from the story in John 4:5-24. (Some of these statements may be false or not directly related to this teaching.)

- ☐ Jesus may reject you after you have failed in relationships.
- ☐ Your marriage problems aren't very important to God.
- ☐ Jesus has compassion if you are struggling in relationships.
- ☐ Marriage can be fully successful without God.
- ☐ Marriage was created by government and society.
- ☐ Marriage is only successful when it honors God's plan.
- ☐ The most important issue in marriage is passion and chemistry.
- ☐ The most important issue in marriage is being happy.
- ☐ The most important issue in marriage is relating with God.

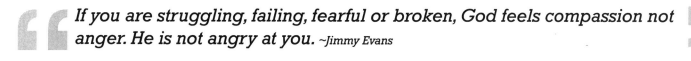

> *If you are struggling, failing, fearful or broken, God feels compassion not anger. He is not angry at you.* ~Jimmy Evans

Fill in the blanks from Jimmy's teaching:

Deep Need #1 - _____

I am loved and _____ for who I am.

Deep Need #2 - _____

I am special, unique, and _____.

Deep Need #3 - _____

I am safe and _____ from harm.

Deep Need #4 - _____

I have a significant _____ and there is a reason for my life.

The Principle of Transference - If we don't _____ _____ to meet our deepest needs, we will automatically _____ the expectation of those needs to those closest to us, especially our _____.

When you depend on others to meet your deepest needs:

1. You will never be _____.

2. You will become _____ and _____.

3. You will become _____ toward people and _____ them for not meeting your expectations.

How to experience a personal relationship with Jesus:

1. Remember that Jesus is a _____ of _____ from God.

2. _____ _____ for what you need.

3. Have faith in God's _____ and _____.

Remember, you will never deserve a relationship with God. Even on your best day, you will always come up short next to Him. You will make mistakes and need forgiveness. The good news is, Jesus loves you exactly the way you are. So if you are struggling in life or in relationships, He wants to give you new life today.

WALK IT OUT:
COUPLE HOME DISCUSSION

Please discuss these questions with your spouse during the upcoming week. You will want to find a time that is good for both of you to talk so that you can give each other your best. This may be during a planned communication time or while on a date night.

1. Tell your spouse something that you love about them. It may be something that you haven't said in a long time. (If you can't remember a specific reason, think back to a positive experience when you were dating.)

HIM: Something I love about you is...

HER: Something I love about you is...

2. On a scale of 1 to 10, rate the level of intimacy and satisfaction in your relationship.

HIM: I would rate the intimacy in our marriage as...

No Intimacy   Great Intimacy

| 1 | 2 | 3 | 4 | 5 | 6 | 7 | 8 | 9 | 10 |

HER: I would rate the intimacy in our marriage as...

No Intimacy   Great Intimacy

| 1 | 2 | 3 | 4 | 5 | 6 | 7 | 8 | 9 | 10 |

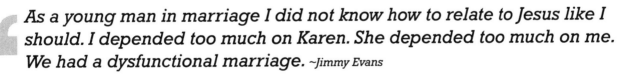

As a young man in marriage I did not know how to relate to Jesus like I should. I depended too much on Karen. She depended too much on me. We had a dysfunctional marriage. ~Jimmy Evans

3. Identify an area of your marriage that you would like to see improve over the next few weeks as you go through this workbook together. For example, you might like to communicate more or desire to overcome a specific issue in your relationship.

HIM: I would like our marriage to improve in the area(s) of...

HER: I would like our marriage to improve in the area(s) of...

4. The woman at the well had been married five times and had given up on marriage. Even today, why do so many people lose hope and believe that marriage doesn't work any more?

HIM: I think men give up on marriage because...

HER: I think women give up on marriage because...

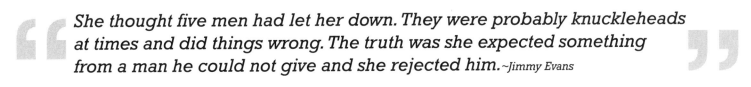

She thought five men had let her down. They were probably knuckleheads at times and did things wrong. The truth was she expected something from a man he could not give and she rejected him. ~Jimmy Evans

5. An unrealistic expectation of marriage is that our spouse will meet all of our needs. The reality is we should be depending on God to meet our deepest needs.

We have four basic needs: acceptance, identity, security and purpose. Which of these needs are you seeking most right now in your life?

HIM: Of my four deepest needs, I'm seeking...

HER: Of my four deepest needs, I'm seeking...

6. Jimmy shared that if we aren't trusting God to meet our deepest needs then we will usually transfer the responsibility to meet those needs to another person. When have you transferred the expectations of your life to someone other than your spouse?

HIM: I expected another person to meet my needs when...

HER: I expected another person to meet my needs when...

7. Now tell your spouse about a time when you were expecting them to meet your deepest needs instead of God. Talk to your spouse about your mistakes and ask for their forgiveness.

HIM: The result of expecting my wife to meet my deepest needs has been...

HER: The result of expecting my husband to meet my deepest needs has been...

8. Even if you are a Christian, it doesn't automatically mean you are putting Christ first. In practical terms, place a check mark next to those areas that are currently a part of your regular schedule.

HIM	HER	
☐	☐	Praying alone
☐	☐	Praying as a couple
☐	☐	Reading scripture
☐	☐	Memorizing scripture
☐	☐	Reading Christian books
☐	☐	Reading devotions
☐	☐	Attending church
☐	☐	Participating in a small group
☐	☐	Spending time with God daily
☐	☐	Serving the needy
☐	☐	Giving of your time or posessions
☐	☐	Mentoring or helping others
☐	☐	Other _____
☐	☐	Other _____
☐	☐	Other _____

HIM: In the weeks to come, I can make God a bigger part of my life by...

HER: In the weeks to come, I can make God a bigger part of my life by...

" *There have been times that you transferred the expectations of your life to people and you set them up for failure because they could not be Jesus to you.* ~Jimmy Evans "

9. In marriage, we have to learn to stop responding in fear and begin responding in faith. What is a step you can take to begin responding in faith and have a more positive outlook on your relationship? Focus on yourself and how you can change.

HIM: I can have a more positive perspective on our marriage by having the faith that...

HER: I can have a more positive perspective on our marriage by having the faith that...

10. One of the most impactful disciplines in your marriage is for you and your spouse to pray together. It not only shows that you trust God, but it also opens the door for Him to heal any hurts and build intimacy in your marriage. How can prayer become a greater emphasis in your relationship?

HIM: I can make prayer a bigger part of my marriage by...

HER: I can make prayer a bigger part of my marriage by...

When you have a problem where do you go first: a friend, the web, a credit card, the store? It does not matter if you love Jesus. It does not matter if you believe in Jesus. Do you trust Him? ~Jimmy Evans

Now that you've talked about prayer, take the next step. Hold your spouse's hand and pray together about how you can make God the most important issue in your marriage.

Couple Prayer: *God, we put our trust in you to meet our deepest needs. Help us forgive each other for mistakes of the past. Today, we choose to make you the center of our marriage and family. Help us do the right thing first and believe for the best in each other. Begin healing any disappointments and frustrations in our marriage as we start this new journey. Amen.*

WRAP IT UP

Only Jesus can meet our deepest needs for acceptance, identity, security and purpose. Our spouse can never meet these needs, and if we expect them to do so, we'll end up disappointed, frustrated and bitter.

God is the only one who can empower us to relate successfully with others long-term. He is the only one who heals our hurts and fills us with unconditional love.

When we admit our mistakes and share our weaknesses, we are drawn closer together. Our mate becomes the "completer" in our relationship as God intended.

When I have been with God I am a different husband than when I have not. Sometimes Karen will say to me when I am not having one of my better days, "Did you pray this morning?" ~Jimmy Evans

SESSION TWO

THE FOUR FOUNDATIONAL LAWS OF MARRIAGE

*Marriage works
when you do it God's way.*

While many people desperately want a marriage that succeeds, fewer and fewer really believe that it can happen for them. It's difficult to find successful marriages when there are so many casualties in relationships.

You've probably asked yourself, "How can I know that we are going to make it? I want our marriage to succeed and not end up as another divorce statistic."

No one gets married just to see their relationship fail a few years later. We marry in order to spend our lives with someone, not to experience a mediocre marriage or the devastation of divorce. What makes it even more sad is that divorce is totally unnecessary. People want to succeed in marriage, they just don't know how.

Few realize that God created marriage based on four foundational laws. When you obey these laws, you can know that your marriage will succeed…

DVD TEACHING WITH JIMMY EVANS

Below is an outline of today's teaching. Feel free to take additional notes in the space provided as you listen to Jimmy share biblical truths on having a successful marriage.

THE FOUR FOUNDATIONAL LAWS OF MARRIAGE

Related Scriptures: *Genesis 2:24-25, Exodus 34:14, Exodus 16:4, Revelation 3:3, 1 Corinthians 7:3-4*

Law #1: The Law of Priority

a) Marriage is designed to operate as the top priority, except for your personal relationship with God. If marriage is not your top priority, it does not work.

b) Legitimate jealousy is a protective warning when something else becomes more important than your relationship.

c) After several years of marriage, men typically focus on their career and women focus on the home and children. These are all good, but they aren't more important than the marriage.

d) How to establish and maintain right priorities in your marriage:

1) Priorities must be proven in real terms, not just words.

Four ways we prove priorities:

(a) Sacrifice – "I will give this up for you."

(b) Time – "I will spend quality time with you."

(c) Energy – "I will meet your needs."

(d) Attitude – "I want to be with you."

2) Priorities must be constantly protected from good things out of priority.

The proper order of priorities is: God, marriage, children, church, extended family and friends, work, hobbies and interests.

Law #2 – The Law of Pursuit

a) Marriage is work. You have to work at your relationship. We work hard at pursuing each other when we are dating, but after years of marriage, we often stop working at the relationship.

b) Four common misconceptions about love and romance

1) The Misconception - "If I marry the right person, the emotions will happen naturally and effortlessly throughout our marriage."

The Truth - The best relationships are when two very different people go through hard times and stay together.

2) The Misconception - "If my emotions change toward my spouse, I must have married the wrong person."

The Truth - Your emotions will always be changing, but you are always in control of your will. God's love is based on a decision not an emotion.

3) The Misconception - "Positive events, experiences and actions should fuel the relationship and our emotions long term."

The Truth - Marriage requires work every day. Men often think they have to "score points" to make their wife happy not realizing that all points evaporate at midnight.

4) The Misconception - "When we have no emotions or have fallen out of love, there is no way to get the love back."

The Truth - Your love can return if you:
    (1) Remember when you pursued each other.
    (2) Ask your spouse for forgiveness.
    (3) Do what you did at the beginning.

The Law of Possession

a) God created marriage for you and your spouse to share everything. Everything that you owned before marriage, you now share together.

b) Common ways we violate the law of possession:

1) Dominance – "If you don't agree, you'll pay a price."

    (1) Disproportionate control of the marriage (money, children, sex, possessions, relationships, spiritual life and atmosphere of the home).

    (2) Men and women are total equals, but both can be dominant.

(3) We dominate through our personality, intimidation and manipulation.

2) Independence – "I'll do my own thing."

(1) The use of the words "mine" and "yours" can destroy relationships.

(2) Some couples spend more time alone in their home than together.

(3) Selfishness destroys relationships. Selflessness builds marriage.

3) Protection – "I don't trust you in some areas."

(1) When a spouse is out of control or passive in an area, it is common for the other spouse to take control and react to the opposite extreme.

(2) Some people use their children, money or sex as a controlling aspect of the relationship.

c) How to establish the law of possession in your marriage:

1) Ask your spouse to give you input concerning the issues of your life and the decisions of the family.

2) Never make an important decision without the input and agreement of your spouse.

Law #4 – The Law of Purity

a) God designed marriage to function in an atmosphere of total nakedness: physically, emotionally, mentally and spiritually.

b) When you have purity in your relationship, you can trust each other with your differences and the most sensitive areas of your life.

c) Your spouse should be your safe place. You should be able to talk about any issue together without giving each other any shame.

d) How to create an atmosphere of purity:

1) We must be careful in what we say and do.

2) We must take responsibility for our own mistakes.

(1) Learn to quickly say, "I'm sorry, I was wrong. Will you forgive me?"

(2) The most healing words in marriage are the words, "I'm sorry."

ADDITIONAL NOTES FROM TODAY'S TEACHING

TALK IT OUT:
COUPLE HOME ACTIVITY

Review the highlights from the video session of *Marriage on the Rock* with your spouse. Look over your outline on the previous pages if needed and answer the following questions.

Fill in the blanks from Jimmy's teaching:

Law #1 – The Law of _____

God designed marriage to operate as the top _____, except for your personal relationship with God.

_____ _____ is a protective warning when something else becomes more important than your relationship.

After several years of marriage, men typically focus on their _____ and women focus on the _____ and _____. These are all good, but they aren't more important than the marriage.

We prove our priorities in four ways: _____, _____, _____ and _____.

Law #2 – The Law of _____

The Misconception - "If I marry the right person, the emotions will happen naturally and effortlessly throughout our marriage."

The Truth - The best relationships are when two very different people go through _____ _____ and _____ _____.

The Misconception - "If my emotions change toward my spouse, I must have married the wrong person."

The Truth - Your emotions will always be _____, but you are always in control of your _____.

The Misconception – "Positive events, experiences and actions should fuel the relationship and our emotions long term."

The Truth - Marriage requires _____ every day.

The Misconception - "When we have no emotions or have fallen out of love, there is no way to get the love back."

The Truth – Your love can return if you:

(1) Remember when you _____ each other.

(2) Ask your spouse for _____.

(3) Do what you did at the _____.

Law #3 – The Law of _____

Everything that you owned before marriage, you now _____ together.

We can violate this law in three ways: through _____, _____ and _____.

Never make an important _____ without the _____ and _____ of your spouse.

Law #4 – The Law of _____

When you observe this law, you can _____ each other with your _____ and the most _____ areas of your life.

We must be _____ in what we _____ and _____. We must take _____ for our own _____.

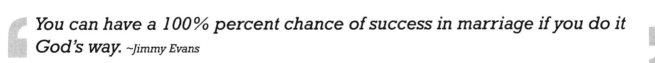

You can have a 100% percent chance of success in marriage if you do it God's way. ~Jimmy Evans

WALK IT OUT:
COUPLE HOME DISCUSSION

Please discuss these questions with your spouse during the upcoming week. You will want to find a time that is good for both of you to talk so that you can give each other your best. This may be during a planned communication time or while on a date night.

1. Think back to when you and your spouse were dating. Share three ways that your spouse prioritized and pursued you before marriage. Listen to each other and discuss.

HIM: When we were dating, my wife pursued me by...

1.

2.

3.

HER: When we were dating, my husband pursued me by...

1.

2.

3.

> *You can't just say, "You're first in my life." You have to prove that your spouse is first.*
> ~Jimmy Evans

Review the list your spouse wrote. If you are still pursuing your spouse the way they listed, put a check by that number. If it's something you are not currently doing, then draw a circle around that number.

2. Lovingly, tell your spouse how you would like them to pursue you in your relationship today.

HIM: I would love it if my wife would pursue me by...

HER: I would love it if my husband would pursue me by...

3. How have your priorities changed since the beginning of your marriage?

HIM: When we married, I was focused on...

HER: When we married, I was focused on...

> *Karen and I had a real problem early in our marriage with golf. And I hung up my golf clubs for several years, and it healed our marriage.*
>
> ~Jimmy Evans

4. If you allow anything or anyone, no matter how good or important, to take the time and energy that rightfully belongs to your spouse you are violating God's design for marriage.

HIM: When do you feel legitimately jealous of something or someone in your wife's life?

HER: When do you feel legitimately jealous of something or someone in your husband's life?

5. Choose one of the four areas of priority: sacrifice, time, energy and attitude. Which one does your spouse do best? Which area would you like to see improve?

HIM: My wife shows me priority most by...

I would like my wife to make me a bigger priority by giving more...

HER: My husband shows me priority most by...

I would like my husband to make me a bigger priority by giving more...

> **The best marriages are two very different people who roll up their sleeves and go through lots of trouble. But they stay together and work it out and come out as best friends.** *~Jimmy Evans*

6. Now that you've heard what your spouse needs from you, how can you make your spouse a greater priority in your life?

HIM: I will make my wife a greater priority by...

For her, I am willing to sacrifice...

HER: I will make my husband a greater priority by...

For him, I am willing to sacrifice...

7. Think about some of the key ways you divide responsibilities in your home. Men, put an X on each of the lines below to indicate how dominant you are in each of the areas. Ladies, please put a check on each of the lines to indicate your level of dominance.

MONEY	Not Dominant _____	Dominant
PARENTING	Not Dominant _____	Dominant
BIG DECISIONS	Not Dominant _____	Dominant
CHORES	Not Dominant _____	Dominant
SEX	Not Dominant _____	Dominant

8. How can you adjust your roles so that you share more equally in your relationship?

HIM: I can share more equally with my wife by...

HER: I can share more equally with my husband by...

Some of the most healing words in a relationship are when we say "I'm sorry" and take responsibility for our mistakes. If you feel ready, apologize to your spouse for mistakes that you've made. Make listening to your spouse's feelings a bigger priority in your relationship.

9. Jimmy says that we should never make a "significant' decision without our spouse.

HIM: I like when my wife includes me when she makes decisions about...

I trust her to make a decision without me concerning...

HER: I like when my husband includes me when he makes decisions about...

I trust him to make a decision without me concerning...

> **When the grass looks greener on the other side, it's time to water your own yard.**
> ~Jimmy Evans

10. Having purity in your marriage means that your spouse has the freedom to confront or talk about any issue. If your spouse doesn't feel comfortable to talk about something, this will limit the level of purity in your marriage. Is there an area of your life that is difficult to talk about? If so, lovingly admit that area to your spouse.

HIM: In order to talk openly, I need from my wife...

HER: In order to talk openly, I need from my husband...

11. How would you rate the quality of your sex life? How is your sex life affected by the current level of purity in your relationship?

HIM: I would rate the quality of our sex life as...

No Intimacy								Great Intimacy	
1	2	3	4	5	6	7	8	9	10

HER: I would rate the quality of our sex life as...

No Intimacy								Great Intimacy	
1	2	3	4	5	6	7	8	9	10

12. Share with your spouse one change they can make that will create more purity in your relationship whether that's physical, emotional, mental or spiritual. Listen to what your spouse has to say and if you feel ready, make it a priority to change in this area.

HIM: A change my wife can make to create more purity in our relationship is...

HER: A change my husband can make to create more purity in our relationship is...

Couple Prayer: *God, we thank you for loving us and giving us laws to ensure that we succeed in marriage. Give us your wisdom as we prioritize and pursue each other. Help us talk about our feelings of jealousy as we make sacrifices in our relationship. Make us so united that there is no "his" or "hers" but only "ours." Remind us to be quick to apologize when we have hurt each other. Help us listen and talk about any issue together. We believe that even better days are ahead. Amen.*

WRAP IT UP

God has created marriage based on four foundational laws. He will bless and protect every couple that honors these laws. Even though you may be convinced that your spouse has most of the problems, you cannot change your spouse, you can only change you.

Listen carefully to the warning signs from your spouse when your priorities are in the wrong order. Pursuing your spouse isn't just for special occasions, it's a daily decision that you are going to work on the relationship so that your marriage gets better year-after-year. True intimacy comes from two people creating an atmosphere where they can share everything and admit that they need each other.

SESSION THREE

UNDERSTANDING AND MEETING YOUR SPOUSE'S NEEDS

*Our different needs
can bring us together.*

When a spouse is fulfilled and happy in their marriage it is usually because their needs are getting met. Whereas when someone is frustrated and disillusioned, it's almost always because some of their needs are being neglected.

When a man expresses a legitimate need for sex, he's actually asking his wife to understand him in a way that no one else does. Rejecting him because his needs are different ruins an opportunity for you both to experience intimacy.

Likewise when a wife expresses a need for detailed communication and her husband rejects her need, she feels devalued and immediately disconnects with him.

Man or woman, each of us has four basic needs. Our needs are intentionally very different from each other. When you understand what your spouse needs from you the most, you'll find the key to your spouse's heart...

DVD TEACHING WITH JIMMY EVANS

Below is an outline of today's teaching. Feel free to take additional notes in the space provided as you listen to Jimmy share biblical truths on having a successful marriage.

UNDERSTANDING AND MEETING YOUR SPOUSE'S NEEDS

Related Scriptures: *Ephesians 5:22-33, 1 Peter 3:1-5, Proverbs 31, 1 Corinthians 7:4*

Major Problems in Meeting Each Other's Needs:

a) Rejection of the inherent differences between the opposite sex.

b) Translation of needs into your own language results in rejection.

c) Selfishness destroys marriage. The best marriage is two servants in love.

His #1 Need – Honor

a) "Wives, submit yourselves to your husbands, as to the Lord." - Ephesians 5:22, NET

b) Men gravitate to where they get the most honor, whether it's at home, work or somewhere else. Men will naturally avoid disrespect.

c) How to give your husband honor:

    1) Allow him to make mistakes or fail (unless it's self-destructive behavior).

    2) Confront in love, but let God be the enforcer.

    3) Honor him where you want him to be, not where he is. (Prov. 31)

    4) Cover his faults and focus on his strengths. Honor always encourages.

His #2 Need – Sex

a) Men give affection to get sex. Women give sex to get affection.

b) How to meet your husband's need for sex:

1) Communicate to your husband that you accept his sexual needs and that you are committed to meeting them.

2) Men are visually and physically stimulated. Men want to see their wife's body while most women are uncomfortable with their bodies.

3) Be more sexual than you feel and be creative. Men have the need for sex and women have the gift of sex. You spouse's needs won't always match your desires.

His #3 Need – Fun and Friendship

a) Your husband will be open with you to the extent that you are having fun together.

b) How to establish friendship:

1) Be his friend and his wife, don't mother him.

2) Find something in common that you both enjoy. Even if it's not your favorite activity, do something that he enjoys.

His #4 Need – Support at Home

a) Men need to do their equal share of the work in the home, especially if both spouses work. A husband's work is not done when he gets home.

b) How to support your husband at home:

1) Women have the gift of nesting. A man needs his wife to create and maintain an atmosphere in their home that causes him to want to be there.

2) Women need to be domestically centered and diligent including meals, housekeeping and homemaking.

Her #1 Need – Security

a) "Husbands, love your wives, just as Christ also loved the Church and gave Himself up for her." - Ephesians 5:25, NASB

b) Women feel most secure when they are married to a sacrificial, sensitive man. Women are most insecure when they are married to a selfish, detached man.

c) How to meet a woman's need for security:

1) Communicate your commitment to sacrifice and meet her needs.

2) Be sensitive to your wife's needs and don't make her ask or beg to get her needs and desires met.

3) Be a faithful provider and money manager.

Her #2 Need – Non-Sexual Affection

a) The softer, non-sexual affection women receive the more sexual they become. This is very difficult for men to understand, but it's true.

b) How to meet your wife's need for soft, non-sexual affection:

1) Be physically affectionate. She needs her husband to hold her hand, put his arm around her gently, hold her and cuddle her.

2) Listen to her when she tells you how she wants to be held.

3) Be gentle and patient. If a man is rough and aggressive, she will feel devalued.

Her #3 Need – Open and Honest Communication

a) Men give short headline answers, but a woman wants detailed answers. Just like men connect through fun and sex, she connects by sharing thoughts and feelings.

b) How to meet your wife's need for communication:

1) Plan regular scheduled time to talk alone with your wife.

2) Be a good listener without distractions.

3) Answer questions fully and speak from your heart.

Her #4 Need – Leadership

a) Leadership means being the loving initiator without dominating the family.

b) How to meet your wife's need for leadership:

1) Lead the children with consistent, loving discipline.

2) Lead with romance. Make your wife feel special and loved.

3) Lead with finances. Oversee the finances and do not overspend.

4) Lead spiritually by attending church as a family and praying together.

ADDITIONAL NOTES FROM TODAY'S TEACHING

_____

_____

_____

_____

_____

_____

_____

_____

_____

_____

_____

_____

_____

_____

_____

_____

_____

_____

_____

_____

TALK IT OUT:
COUPLE HOME ACTIVITY

Review the highlights from the video session of *Marriage on the Rock* with your spouse. Look over your outline on the previous pages if needed and answer the following questions.

Ladies, fill in the blanks from Jimmy's teaching on meeting your husband's needs:

His #1 Need – _____

Men gravitate to where they get the most _____, whether it's at _____, _____ or somewhere else. Men will naturally avoid _____.

How to meet your husband's need:

(1) Allow him to make _____ or _____.

(2) Confront in love, but let God be the _____.

(3) Honor him where you _____ _____ to _____, not where he _____.

(4) Cover his _____ and focus on his _____.

His #2 Need – _____

How to meet your husband's need:

(1) Communicate to your husband that you _____ his sexual needs and that you are _____ to meeting them.

(2) Men are _____ and _____ stimulated.

(3) Be more _____ than you feel and be _____. Men have the _____ for sex and women have the _____ of sex. You spouse's needs won't always match your desires.

His #3 Need – _____ and _____

How to meet your husband's need:

(1) Be his _____ and his wife, don't _____ him.

(2) Find something in _____ that you both _____. Even if it's not your favorite activity, do something that he _____.

His #4 Need – _____ at _____

How to meet your husband's need:

(1) Women have the gift of _____. A man needs his wife to create and _____ an atmosphere in their home that causes him to _____ to be there.

(2) Women need to be domestically centered and diligent including _____, _____ and _____.

Guys, fill in the blanks from Jimmy's teaching on meeting your wife's needs:

Her #1 Need – _____

Women feel most _____ when they are married to a _____, _____ man.
Women are most _____ when they are married to a _____, _____ man.

How to meet your wife's need:

(1) Communicate your _____ to _____ and meet her needs.

(2) Be sensitive to your wife's needs and don't make her _____ or _____.

(3) Be a _____ provider and money _____.

Her #2 Need – _____ _____

How to meet your wife's need:

(1) Be physically affectionate. She needs you to _____ her _____, put your _____ around her _____, _____ her and cuddle her.

(2) _____ to her when she tells you how she wants to be _____.

(3) Be gentle and patient. If a man is _____ and _____, she will feel _____.

Her #3 Need – _____ and _____ _____

How to meet your wife's need:

(1) Plan regular _____ time to _____ alone your wife.

(2) Be a good _____ without distraction.

(3) Answer questions _____ and speak from your _____.

Her #4 Need – _____

How to meet your wife's need:

(1) Lead the _____ with consistent, loving _____.

(2) Lead with _____. Make your wife feel _____ and _____.

(3) Lead with _____. Oversee the finances and do not _____.

(4) Lead _____ by attending _____ as a family and _____ together.

WALK IT OUT:
COUPLE HOME DISCUSSION

Work on these questions separately and then discuss your answers with your spouse during the upcoming week. You will want to find a time that is good for both of you to talk so that you can give each other your best. This may be during a planned communication time or while on a date night.

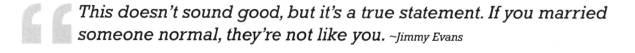

This doesn't sound good, but it's a true statement. If you married someone normal, they're not like you. ~*Jimmy Evans*

WIVES

1. What potential did you see in your husband while you were dating? What are some of the best qualities you see in him today?

2. Just like the Proverbs 31 wife honored her husband even when he didn't deserve it, how can you honor your husband?

3. Remember a truly romantic experience the two of you had together. What did you do to show that you cared about your husband's sexual needs? How could you express that to him again?

4. How did you and your husband have fun at the beginning of your relationship? What activities make your husband happy today?

5. As a wife, what is the biggest challenge around the home: meals, housekeeping or homemaking? How would you like your husband to support you more in these areas?

> *Most people take the energy that God gave them to love each other, trying to change each other. In many marriages it's a battle. Who's going to win?* ~Jimmy Evans

6. Now let's switch gears and focus on your needs. How did your husband sacrifice and show you love early in your relationship?

7. How does your husband show you love and security today? What additional expressions of romance and sacrifice would you like to see from your husband?

8. What kinds of non-sexual affection do you like to receive from your husband? (If he doesn't know exactly what you need, lovingly tell him.) How do you communicate to your husband when you need non-sexual affection without it leading to sex?

9. Do you need your husband to communicate more about his thoughts and feelings? How could you create a safe atmosphere for him to share with you?

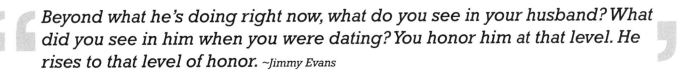

Beyond what he's doing right now, what do you see in your husband? What did you see in him when you were dating? You honor him at that level. He rises to that level of honor. ~Jimmy Evans

10. In what area of leadership would you like your husband to either take a more active role (or a less dominate role) in your marriage: children, romance, finances or spiritual matters? Be specific.

HUSBANDS

1. Men, how did your wife honor and respect you early in your relationship?

2. Men, list some ways that you like your wife to show you honor and respect.

1.

2.

3.

> *The standard for women is to respect your husband like you would Jesus. The standard for men is to give your life for her. Love her more than yourself.* ~Jimmy Evans

3. Remember a romantic experience you had together that truly met your sexual needs. What did your wife do for you? How could you help your wife recreate that type of experience?

4. How did you and your wife have fun at the beginning of your relationship? How do you and your wife have fun together today? Is there something new you would like your wife to do with you?

5. What, if anything, could your wife do to make your home a more inviting place for you?

6. Now let's switch gears and focus on your wife's needs. What potential did you see in your wife when you were dating? What are some of the best qualities you see in her today?

> *Karen was sitting across the room one day folding clothes, and the Lord just impressed on me. Walk over and put your arm around her and nothing beyond that. I'd never done that before.* ~Jimmy Evans

7. Jimmy says that creating security requires sacrifice. What are you currently sacrificing for her? Is there something you could sacrifice that you aren't currently doing?

8. Can you relate with Jimmy's story of the first time he showed Karen non-sexual affection? Whether cuddling, holding hands or putting your arm around her, when could you give your wife non-sexual affection?

9. When do you and your wife usually talk? What times of the week could you set aside for more quality communication without interruptions?

> *Women need to be more sexual than they feel and meet their husband's need for sex. Likewise, men need to communicate more than they feel.*
> ~Jimmy Evans

10. Men are supposed to be the loving, sacrificial leaders in the home. Everyone should come before you. How can you lead more (or be less dominant) concerning children, romance, finances or spiritual matters? What could you change to be the loving initiator in any of the above areas?

1.

2.

3.

Couple Prayer: *God, you made men and women very different. Help us stop trying to change each other and accept each other's different needs. Begin to open the lines of communication as we focus on meeting the needs of our spouse. Whether honor or security, sexual or non-sexual, we choose to focus on our spouse and not on ourself. We will no longer try to change each other. We accept each other as we are. Amen.*

WRAP IT UP

When a woman gives her husband honor and meets his needs, it fills his world and draws him back to his wife. Many women are waiting to honor their husbands until they see change in his heart. This is backwards from what God says. Only the Lord can change your husband, but you can be the agent of that change by praising him for what he does right.

Just like men need their wives to be honoring and fun, women need men to sacrificially love them. By following Christ's example to be a servant leader, men can fulfill their wife's desires and reignite the passion in their relationship. For a man, meeting your wife's needs is not just a matter of responsibility, it is the basis for romance and spiritual connection in your relationship.

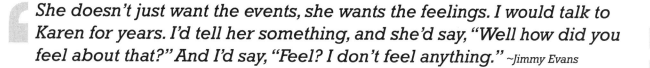

She doesn't just want the events, she wants the feelings. I would talk to Karen for years. I'd tell her something, and she'd say, "Well how did you feel about that?" And I'd say, "Feel? I don't feel anything." ~Jimmy Evans

DESTRUCTIVE HUSBANDS AND WIVES

You can disarm destructive
behaviors in your relationship.

We are all human. We have pain from our past. We have faults and have made mistakes. Even when we have the best intentions, we can deeply hurt each other in marriage.

What makes destructive behavior even more dangerous is that it is usually justified with our reasoning. We rationalize with our excuses. "I'm doing this because of what you are doing wrong." Or even "You have wrong expectations of me." If blaming our spouse doesn't work, we may even say, "This is just the way I am. Deal with it."

Regardless of how we justify our actions, half of all marriages are destroyed from within, while many more suffer needlessly. To achieve your dreams of having a secure and satisfying marriage, you have to deal with any negative tendencies you may have.

You can become an overcomer...

DVD TEACHING WITH JIMMY EVANS

Below is an outline of today's teaching. Feel free to take additional notes in the space provided as you listen to Jimmy share biblical truths on having a successful marriage.

DESTRUCTIVE HUSBANDS AND WIVES

Related Scriptures: *Hosea 4:6a, Luke 6:28, 1 Corinthians 15:33, Proverbs 18:21-22, Hebrews 13:4-5*

The Four Reasons We Become Destructive

a) Ignorance – We don't know any better.

   1) "My people are destroyed for lack of knowledge." - Hosea 4:6a, NKJV

   2) Successful people don't hide their weaknesses, they admit them.

b) Past Hurts – We all have pain from our past that shapes us. Parental hurts, romantic hurts and life hurts are especially damaging.

   1) Truths about unhealed hurts:

      (1) Hurts hinder intimacy and are a breeding ground for fear and shame.

      (2) Hurts cause us to react to our spouse in extreme and unhealthy ways.

      (3) Hurts cause a distortion of reality where we don't see the nature of our behavior and the problems they are causing.

   2) Steps to overcoming your hurts:

      (1) Be honest about your hurts. Bring everything into the light.

      (2) Admit your issues. Focus on yourself and take responsibility.

      (3) Forgive those who have hurt you.

         (a) Stop judging or punishing someone else for their mistakes.

         (b) The secret to healing is blessing the person who has hurt you.

         (c) Forgiveness doesn't make someone right, it just makes you free.

SESSION FOUR: DESTRUCTIVE HUSBANDS AND WIVES

c) Bad Friends and Negative Influences – Your friends predict your future.

    1) Adultery, divorce, and destructive behaviors run in groups.

    2) Church is not a place for people who do not have issues. Church should be a place where people are dealing with their issues.

d) Defensiveness – Giving your spouse the freedom to complain will diffuse defensiveness.

    1) When you are defensive, you don't allow your spouse to process problems.

    2) If you and your spouse don't agree, it's difficult to validate or acknowledge their concerns and feelings.

    3) It's easier to blame your spouse than admit that some of the problem may be you.

The Four Main Destructive Behaviors in Marriage

a) Criticism – It's the number one predictor of divorce

    1) Complaining ("I feel _____.") vs. Criticism ("You did _____.")

    2) How to deal with criticism:

        (1) Follow the 10 to 1 rule. "I will praise you ten times for every time I complain. I will never become critical."

        (2) "I will take responsibility to build your self-esteem. I take responsibility for my language and will never blame you or anyone else for it."

b) Control and Dominance – Satisfaction drops when there is control.

    1) God created marriage as an equal partnership and that's how it works best.

    2) How to deal with control and dominance:

        (1) Make all decisions together. Never make your spouse pay a price for disagreeing. Ask for their input.

        (2) If you are dominant, sit down. If you are more passive, stand up.

c) Checking Out – Marriage is a lifelong covenant.

    1) "I will never leave you nor forsake you." - Hebrews 13:5, NKJV

    2) Forsake means "turn your heart away." You can forsake your spouse without leaving them.

3) How to deal with checking out:

(1) Commit to never leaving or turning your heart away.

(2) Make marriage your number one priority.

d) Cruelty and Abuse - We all suffer because of each other.

1) Suffering means discomfort. Abuse means damage with intent.

2) How to deal with abusive behavior:

(1) Stand up and don't allow it. The first time you are a victim. The second time, you are a volunteer.

(2) Seek help immediately from your church, a professional Christian counselor and stable friends and family.

(3) If necessary, temporarily separate and communicate your desire for reconciliation if your spouse gets help and demonstrates change.

ADDITIONAL NOTES FROM TODAY'S TEACHING

_____

_____

_____

_____

_____

_____

_____

_____

_____

_____

TALK IT OUT:
COUPLE HOME ACTIVITY

Review the highlights from the video session of *Marriage on the Rock* with your spouse. Look over your outline on the previous pages if needed and answer the following questions.

Fill in the blanks from Jimmy's teaching:

The Four Reasons We Become Destructive

(1) _____ - We don't _____ any better.

(2) _____ _____ - We all have pain that shapes us, especially _____ hurts, _____ hurts and _____ hurts.

(3) Bad _____ and negative _____ - _____ predict your future.

(4) _____ - Giving your spouse the freedom to _____ will diffuse defensiveness.

Steps to Overcoming Past Hurts

(1) Be _____ about your hurts. Bring _____ into the _____.

(2) _____ your issues. Focus on _____ and take _____.

(3) _____ those who have hurt you. The secret to healing is _____ the person who has hurt you.

The Four Main Destructive Behaviors in Marriage

(1) _____ - It's the number one _____ of divorce.

(2) _____ and _____ - Satisfaction drops when there is _____.

(3) _____ Out – Marriage is a lifelong _____.

(4) _____ and _____ - We all _____ because of each other.

Read each pair of statements aloud and write beside it whether it's a complaint or a criticism. Complaints are aimed at a specific behavior or event and usually focus on your feelings ("just the facts ma'am"), while criticism attacks a person's character ("you're guilty") and often focuses on many events or a global statement.

_____ I wish you would take out the trash. You never do anything around here.

_____ I could really use your help today. Can you please take out the trash for me?

_____ I should have known not to count on you. Whenever I ask for something from you, I'm always disappointed.

_____ I really felt let down today when you didn't come through.

_____ I know you are busy, but can you pick up the clothes? It would help me feel better about the house.

_____ You are a slob and never do anything right around here.

_____ I can't believe how messy you are. You're just like a child.

_____ Can you help a little more?

_____ You never pay any attention to me. All you care about is TV.

_____ I'm feeling lonely and down tonight. Can we talk for awhile?

_____ I can't believe you forgot our plans. Do you care about this family at all? You only think about yourself.

_____ When I didn't hear from you I was worried something happened. Can you please call me next time so I don't worry?

WALK IT OUT:
COUPLE HOME DISCUSSION

Please discuss these questions with your spouse during the upcoming week. You will want to find a time that is good for both of you to talk so that you can give each other your best. This may be during a planned communication time or while on a date night.

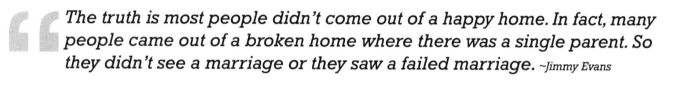

The truth is most people didn't come out of a happy home. In fact, many people came out of a broken home where there was a single parent. So they didn't see a marriage or they saw a failed marriage. ~Jimmy Evans

1. In the teaching, Jimmy challenged every couple to read a marriage book together. (If you don't like to read try an audio book.) What marriage topics would you like to learn more about with your spouse (money, sex, parenting, conflict, etc.)? If your ideas differ, the husband can choose a book for you each to read on "his" topic of choice and then you both can read a book on "her" chosen topic.

HIM: Concerning marriage, I'd like to learn more about...

1.

2.

3.

HER: Concerning marriage, I'd like to learn more about...

1.

2.

3.

2. Everyone has hurts from life. If you still feel pain or disappointment over an event then it needs to be discussed and brought into the light. What are some hurtful or traumatic experiences from your past? Talk about your experiences and feelings with your spouse. (If you need some ideas, remember there are three kinds of hurts: parental hurts, romantic hurts and life hurts.)

HIM: The major hurts in my life are...

1.

2.

3.

HER: The major hurts in my life are...

1.

2.

3.

3. How have these hurts influenced your marriage and how you view relationships?

HIM: Concerning my past relationships I learned...

HER: Concerning my past relationships I learned...

4. Is there a connection to your past hurts and how you seek to control (or avoid control) in certain areas of your marriage? Seeking control or giving up control is usually in response to pain and a desire to not go down the same road again.

HIM: Do you see a correlation to your past hurts and how you seek to control (or avoid control) in your marriage? Why or why not?

HER: Do you see a correlation to your past hurts and how you seek to control (or avoid control) in your marriage? Why or why not?

> *It doesn't matter who you're mad at from your past. You're going to take it out on your spouse the most. Even if you're not mad at your spouse, they're going to get the worst of it.* ~Jimmy Evans

5. Jimmy says that we become like our closest friends and that we need Christian relationships. What friends are most trustworthy in your life? What friends could you turn to if you had significant marriage problems? Discuss how you and your spouse can invest more in these positive friendships.

HIM: My closest friends are...

1.

2.

3.

HER: My closest friends are...

1.

2.

3.

We can invest more in these positive relationships by...

1.

2.

3.

6. An indicator of defensiveness is how our families dealt with problems growing up. How did your parents handle conflict? How does this influence how you talk about issues in your relationship?

HIM: Growing up, my family dealt with conflict by...

HER: Growing up, my family dealt with conflict by...

HIM: Today, I deal with conflict by...

HER: Today, I deal with conflict by...

> *What I thought was, "If I ever show her weakness, the world is going to crumble." When I showed her weakness is when the world came together.*
> ~Jimmy Evans

7. Unforgiveness is one of the biggest destructive behaviors in marriage because we usually take bitterness and hurts out on our spouse. Even if it's yourself, your spouse, your parents or friends, who do you need to forgive and why?

HIM: God, these people have hurt me. I choose to forgive and pray that you will bless them...

1.

2.

3.

HER: God, these people have hurt me. I choose to forgive and pray that you will bless them...

1.

2.

3.

8. Long term criticism is the number one predictor of divorce. Criticism is really the absence of praise and honor. Jimmy suggests saying ten positive things about your spouse every time you say anything negative. You should become intentional about praising your spouse.

> *If I haven't said 10 things positive, I haven't earned the right to complain.*
> *You need to praise a lot more than you criticize.* ~Jimmy Evans

Write down the first ten positive things that come to your mind about your spouse.

HIM: Ten positive things about my wife are:

1.

2.

3.

4.

5.

6.

7.

8.

9.

10.

HER: Ten positive things about my husband are:

1.

2.

3.

4.

5.

6.

7.

8.

9.

10.

9. Criticism can be very damaging to your relationship. You can reverse criticism by giving your spouse the freedom to complain before it becomes contempt. Criticism often implies that you "always" or "never" do something. Whereas a complaint is usually focused on one particular event.

Choose a minor frustration that you have with your spouse. Talk about the issue. Listen to the complaint with an open heart and without getting defensive or frustrated.

HIM: Thank you for giving me the freedom to complain. My minor complaint is...

HER: Thank you for giving me the freedom to complain. My minor complaint is...

10. Now that you've heard your spouse's perspective on the issue, what could you begin to do to make them feel better?

HIM: Concerning my wife's complaint, I can try to make a difference by...

HER: Concerning my husband's complaint, I can try to make a difference by...

> *When you won't let your spouse complain, the problems don't go away, they accumulate.* ~Jimmy Evans

11. Hebrews 13:5 says that God "will never leave you nor forsake you." We're supposed to treat our spouse the same way. Forsake means "turn your heart away." You can turn your heart away and still be physically present. Going forward, how can your spouse keep their heart turned toward you?

HIM: I would like my wife to keep her heart focused on me by...

1.

2.

3.

HER: I would like my husband to keep his heart focused on me by...

1.

2.

3.

12. It's so easy to point the finger at others in our hurt and frustration. What are some things that you could be doing differently to promote health in your marriage? Write down the issues that you see in your own life and give them to the Lord.

HIM: I can better promote health in my marriage by...

1.

2.

3.

HER: I can better promote health in my marriage by...

1.

2.

3.

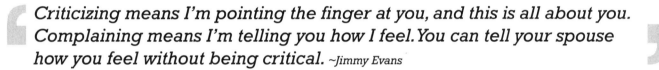

Criticizing means I'm pointing the finger at you, and this is all about you. Complaining means I'm telling you how I feel. You can tell your spouse how you feel without being critical. ~Jimmy Evans

Couple Prayer: *God, whether its criticism, dominance, ignorance or the pain from our past, Lord you know everything that has happened in our lives. Help us overcome the destructive behavior in our marriage so that we can have a fulfilling relationship. We trust you to change our hearts toward one another and towards the people that have hurt us. We forgive and pray blessings over them. Help us eliminate the destructive behaviors in our marriage and replace them with positive words and actions. Amen.*

WRAP IT UP

Whether control, criticism, past hurts or unforgiveness, we can all be destructive in our behavior. We have to realize that we can't change our spouse, but we can take responsibility for ourselves.

Freedom happens when we admit our destructive behaviors to God and each other. Commit to building up your spouse with praise and positive actions. As you do your part, God will heal the destructive areas of your marriage.

SESSION FIVE

THE POWER OF POSITIVE COMMUNICATION

*Good marriages are always based
on positive words.*

Your relationship likely began with good communication. You got to know each other by spending a lot of time talking.

If you are going to have a good marriage, it is always based on a lot of positive words. If there are not many positive words being spoken, your marriage may be on the wrong path. The good news is, it's never too late to change.

Communication is literally the essential element to every great relationship. You simply cannot get to know another human being unless you make the effort to have successful communication...

DVD TEACHING WITH JIMMY EVANS

Below is an outline of today's teaching. Feel free to take additional notes in the space provided as you listen to Jimmy share biblical truths on having a successful marriage.

THE POWER OF
POSITIVE COMMUNICATION

Related Scriptures: *Proverbs 18:20-21, Matthew 12:36-37, Matthew 12:33-35, Psalm 100:4, Proverbs 3:3, Ephesians 4:15, 1 Peter 3:4*

Danger #1 – Not Understanding the Power of Words

a) "A man's stomach shall be satisfied from the fruit of his mouth; from the produce of his lips he shall be filled. Death and life are in the power of the tongue, and those who love it will eat its fruit." - Proverbs 18:20-21, NKJV

b) Words give life and words can kill. God wants to use your mouth to give life and help everyone around you, especially your spouse.

c) "Our words are important to God and have an impact for all eternity. We will be judged according to our words." (Matthew 12:36-37)

d) 5 Common deceptions about communication

1) "Words are evaporative." - Words make a lasting impression. They can impact us for decades.

2) "Words are non-revealing" - Words reveal the real you and the condition of your heart.

3) "Words are substitutionary" - Words cannot replace actions. Be genuine and sincere.

4) "Words are powerless" - Words have a profound impact. The power of life is in your tongue.

5) "Bad words can bring good results." - Angry tirades or profanity will end in a negative result.

Danger #2 – Men and Women Communicate Differently

a) Women need detailed communication, much more than men.

    1) A woman needs communication as much as a man needs sex.

    2) The key to a husband getting his needs met is through meeting his wife's emotional needs.

b) When we talk, men are usually emotionally modest, but women are emotionally immodest. It's the opposite of sex where women are modest and men are immodest.

    1) Men like to talk about surface subjects like cars, sports, electronics and jobs. Women talk about relationships and feelings.

    2) Men need a private and honoring atmosphere in order to talk. He needs to know that his wife will respect his privacy and not repeat what he shares.

c) We hear through our different needs.

    1) A woman hears through her primary need for security and love.

        (1) A woman needs to feel secure in her relationship.

        (2) She needs to hear, "I care and I'm tuned in. I'll do whatever it takes. My heart is turned toward you. I'll say no to anything else."

        (3) When a woman senses that you are disconnected and tuned out, she is hearing insecurity because your heart is not with her.

    2) A man hears through his primary need for honor and respect.

        (1) For a man to open up and talk, he has to feel honor and esteem.

        (2) He needs to hear, "I believe in you. You are a good man. I love you. You are the best. I respect you."

        (3) When a woman makes a man feel like he's a bad man or she's very critical, it jams his communication signals. He won't hear you.

Five Standards of Successful Communication

a) Care - You can't communicate with a person who doesn't care.

    You communicate care by:

        (1) Body language, countenance and tone of voice.

        (2) Being a good listener.

        (3) Giving a kind and appropriate response.

b) Praise - We have to begin with a positive tone.

    1) We enter into each other's heart with praise. (Psalm 100:4)

    2) Say negative things in a positive way. Negativity destroys marriages.

c) Truth - Honesty is an essential foundation of intimacy and trust.

    1) We need mercy and truth. (Proverbs 3:3)

    2) Speak the truth in love. (Ephesians 4:15)

d) Faith – Believe that God is able to enforce the truth in your spouse's heart.

Women can change their husbands without a word.

    (1) "Rather let it be the hidden person of the heart, with the incorruptible beauty of a gentle and quiet spirit, which is very precious in the sight of God." – 1 Peter 3:4, NKJV

    (2) A gentle and quiet spirit means you have faith in God and don't try to be the enforcer.

    (3) Once you speak the truth in love, pray and believe God for the results.

e) Surrender – Decide that your mouth is God's mouth and is dedicated to serving and glorifying Him.

ADDITIONAL NOTES FROM TODAY'S TEACHING

_____

_____

_____

_____

_____

_____

_____

_____

_____

_____

TALK IT OUT:
COUPLE HOME ACTIVITY

Review the highlights from the video session of *Marriage on the Rock* with your spouse. Look over your outline on the previous pages if needed and answer the following questions.

Fill in the blanks from Jimmy's teaching:

Danger #1 – Not Understanding the Power of Words

"A man's stomach shall be satisfied from the fruit of his _____; from the _____ of his lips he shall be filled. _____ and _____ are in the power of the tongue, and those who love it will eat its fruit." - Proverbs 18:20-21, NKJV

Danger #2 – Men and Women Communicate Differently

A woman needs communication as much as a man needs _____. The key to a husband getting his needs met is through meeting his wife's _____ needs.

When we talk, men are usually emotionally _____, but women are emotionally _____. It's the opposite of _____ where women are modest and men are immodest.

A woman hears through her primary need for _____ and love. She needs to hear, "I _____ and I'm _____ in. I'll do _____ it takes."

When a woman senses that you are _____ and tuned out, she is hearing _____ because your _____ is not with her.

A man hears through his primary need for _____ and respect. He needs to hear, "I _____ in you. You are a _____ man."

When a woman makes a man feel like he's a bad man or she's very _____, it _____ his communication signals. He won't _____ you.

Five Standards of Successful Communication

(1) Care - You communicate care by:

1. _____ language, _____ and _____ of voice.

2. Being a good _____.

3. Giving a _____ and appropriate response.

(2) Praise - We have to begin with a positive _____. Say negative things in a _____ way. Negativity _____ marriages.

(3) Truth - Honesty is an essential foundation of intimacy and trust. _____ the truth in love.

(4) Faith - As the wife, a _____ and _____ spirit means you have faith in God and don't try to be the _____. Once you _____ the truth in love, pray and _____ God for the results.

(5) Surrender – Decide that your mouth is _____ _____ and is dedicated to _____ and _____ Him.

WALK IT OUT:
COUPLE HOME DISCUSSION

Please discuss these questions with your spouse during the upcoming week. You will want to find a time that is good for both of you to talk so that you can give each other your best. This may be during a planned communication time or while on a date night.

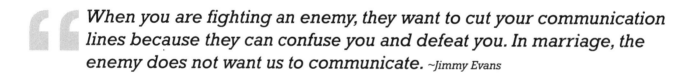

When you are fighting an enemy, they want to cut your communication lines because they can confuse you and defeat you. In marriage, the enemy does not want us to communicate. ~Jimmy Evans

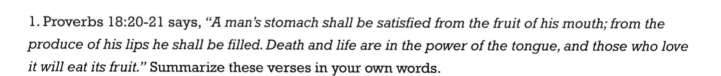

1. Proverbs 18:20-21 says, *"A man's stomach shall be satisfied from the fruit of his mouth; from the produce of his lips he shall be filled. Death and life are in the power of the tongue, and those who love it will eat its fruit."* Summarize these verses in your own words.

HIM: To me, Proverbs 18:20-21 means...

HER: To me, Proverbs 18:20-21 means...

2. What are some words from your spouse that encourage and uplift you?

HIM: Words I love to hear from my wife are...

HER: Words I love to hear from my husband are...

3. What are some words from your spouse that bring you down and discourage you?

HIM: Words that make me feel discouraged are...

HER: Words that make me feel discouraged are...

4. What is most important when you and your spouse talk, their words or their tone? Focus on how you feel when you spouse speaks to you. Discuss this issue and lovingly give your spouse examples.

HIM: When my wife speaks to me, what's most important is…

HER: When my husband speaks to me, what's most important is…

> *When I came home from work I thought she was nosey. She would ask, "Where did you go? What did they say? How did you feel about that?" I was like, "This is a boundary violation."* ~Jimmy Evans

5. When your spouse comes home what is your typical routine? Do you talk with each other about the details of your day immediately, later or not much at all? Talk about your routine and anything you could maybe do differently.

HIM: When I see you, I like it when…

HER: When I see you, I like it when…

6. Do either of you feel frustrated because your spouse doesn't talk to you enough? If so, could improvement be made in this area?

HIM: Communication might improve in our relationship if we began to…

HER: Communication might improve in our relationship if we began to…

7. A man needs a safe environment where he is respected and honored for him to openly share. When and where is the best time for you to talk with each other? When is not a good time?

HIM: For me, the best time for us to talk is when…

HER: For me, the best time for us to talk is when…

> *If you want a man to talk, if you ever tell somebody what we said, we will never tell you anything again. When we open our heart, be careful how you respond because we are very tender on the inside. ~Jimmy Evans*

8. Jimmy discussed how hurtful it is when a wife shares personal information from her husband with family and friends. What kind of information is ok for your wife to share? What kind of information would you prefer she keep private?

HIM: It's ok for my wife to talk about...

HER: It's ok for my husband to share...

HIM: I would be hurt if my wife talked about...

HER: I would be hurt if my husband shared...

> *Karen knows if I am speaking security or not. Here is what she wants to hear, "I care. I am tuned in and I will do whatever it takes. My heart is turned toward you and our family. I will say no to anything else."*
> ~Jimmy Evans

9. When we talk, we show that we care by our: (1) body language, countenance, tone of voice, (2) being a good listener and (3) giving a kind and appropriate response. Which of these areas would you like your spouse to work on for you?

HIM: I like my wife to show me she cares by...

HER: I like my husband to show me he cares by...

10. Praise reminds us of what is good and right in our spouse. Praise your spouse for three things that they have done in the past week for you or for your family.

HIM: I praise my wife for...

1.

2.

3.

HER: I praise my husband for...

1.

2.

3.

11. Do you have any unresolved conflict in your marriage right now? If so, talk about the issue from your perspective.

HIM: For me, an unresolved conflict I'm dealing with is...

HER: For me, an unresolved conflict I'm dealing with is...

If you thought of an area of conflict in your marriage, take some time to discuss the situation. Listen to each other patiently until you understand the other's point of view. Then begin to work toward an agreement that is mutually acceptable. Forgive one another as needed. If you can't agree after several discussions, it may be a good idea to seek wise Christian counsel.

> *I have said this to Karen, "The way you say it, is more important to me than what you are saying." ~Jimmy Evans*

12. Do you and your spouse have a consistent, regular time set aside for talking about your relationship and family? If not, consider how you might fit such a time into your schedule. For example, set aside time to talk without interruptions when the kids have gone to bed. If you do have a regular time for communication, discuss whether there is anything you can do to make it more productive.

We commit to having an uninterrupted time to talk each _____ at _____ o'clock.

_____

His Signature   Date

_____

Her Signature   Date

Couple Prayer: *God, give us understanding and patience as we try to lovingly listen and respond to each other. Help us replace any negative words with uplifting positive speech in our relationship. Forgive us of when we have been selfish. Together, we give you control over our mouths. May our words fulfill our spouse's needs for honor and security. We commit to you and each other that we will regularly meet at our scheduled communication time to talk about important issues. Amen.*

Your body language tells your spouse if you care or not. Your countenance, the way you look at them when they are communicating. If you are rolling your eyes, if you are turning your head away that is not good. ~Jimmy Evans

WRAP IT UP

Communication will always be a defining factor of your marriage. That is why you need to remember that you are married to someone who is different than you and has different needs than you.

Whether its honor or security, learn to encrypt everything you say with words that affirm your spouse's deepest need. Effective communication is the secret of how you fall in love and how you stay in love.

SESSION SIX

FINANCIAL MANAGEMENT IN MARRIAGE

*Your financial perspective
brings balance to your relationship.*

Marriage is usually good for a couple's financial well-being. Because we share our resources and are more likely to make long-term financial decisions, marriage is generally better than being single for our bottom line.

However, finances are one of the greatest areas of tension in a relationship. In fact, a majority of people who divorce list unresolved financial conflict as the primary reason for their separation.

Therefore, it's critical that we understand each other's financial perspective and how we can manage money so that it's a blessing to our marriage...

DVD TEACHING WITH JIMMY EVANS

Below is an outline of today's teaching. Feel free to take additional notes in the space provided as you listen to Jimmy share biblical truths on having a successful marriage.

FINANCIAL MANAGEMENT IN MARRIAGE

Related Scriptures: *Matthew 6:19-34, Mark 4:19, Luke 6:38, Malachi 3:11, Proverbs 10:22, Luke 11:17b, Amos 3:3, Proverbs 29:18a*

Danger #1 – Disregarding the Lordship of Jesus in Your Finances

a) Important truths about God and Money:

1) Money offers us everything that God offers, but without any moral constraints.

2) God's blessing on our finances not only creates peace in our hearts, but it also releases His miracle power to increase and protect us.

3) Putting God first makes Him Lord and stops conflict in marriage.

b) "The blessing of the Lord makes one rich, And He adds no sorrow with it." - Proverbs 10:22, NKJV

1) Prosperity just means having more than enough to do God's will for your life. The amount is personalized for each person.

2) Not having enough is a curse. That is called poverty. Anyone who believes that poverty is a blessing has never lived in poverty.

c) "But seek first the kingdom of God and His righteousness, and all these things shall be added to you." - Matthew 6:33, NKJV

d) If Jesus is Lord of your finances then:

1) You pray about decisions and don't make them without His blessing.

2) You honor God through giving to your local church and others in need.

Danger #2 – Disrespecting Your Spouse's Financial Perspective and Input

a) The "Driver" Money Language

    1) Strength - For the driver, money means success. The driver may have an over dependence on money for self-esteem, confidence and security.

    2) Weakness - Rather than trusting God for identity and purpose, they allow money to meet their needs, thereby making money their God.

    3) Communicates love by showing (house, car, possessions).

b) The "Amiable" Money Language

    1) Strength - For the amiable, money means love. Relationships are the focus of their financial desires. Lack of money means losing the ability to express love.

    2) Weakness - The amiable may be kind and generous, but can be a poor money manager who is unprepared for the long term.

    3) Communicates love by sharing ("what's mine is yours", likes to have fun).

c) The "Analytic" Money Language

    1) Strength - For the analytic, money means security. Money keeps away chaos and problems. Analytics are well structured and good planners.

    2) Weakness - The analytic, though well structured, may be insensitive to the needs of people and the voice of God. May be legalistic and unyielding.

    3) Communicates love by saving (plans for long term goals, invests wisely).

d) The "Expressive" Money Language

    1) Strength - For the expressive, money means acceptance and respect from desirable people. Money provides a basis for relationships.

    2) Weakness - An expressive may use money the way some people use alcohol to hide their fears and insecurities and to deal with their pain.

    3) Communicates love by spending (shopaholic, lives in financial denial).

Danger #3 – Dominance of Money and Financial Decisions

a) It is common for there to be a disproportionate control of the money.

b) Whether man or woman, it is important to be equal partners even if one spouse manages paying the bills.

Danger #4 – Disagreement about Financial Decisions, Priorities and Values

a) It is impossible to disagree and succeed. (Luke 11:17b) Most couples fight about finances because they haven't agreed. (Amos 3:3)

    1) The purpose of creating a budget is so you will have a pro-active conversation in advance. Budgeting forces you to agree beforehand on values.

    2) Three kinds of communication: pro-active, reactive and readioactive.

b) Have an annual vision retreat to talk and pray.

Danger #5 – Debt

a) Only consider borrowing for essential items like a home or car.

b) Save money and live within your means. Save for emergencies.

c) Pay cash for purchases. Only use credit cards if you pay them off monthly.

ADDITIONAL NOTES FROM TODAY'S TEACHING

_____

_____

_____

_____

_____

_____

_____

_____

_____

_____

_____

_____

TALK IT OUT:
COUPLE HOME ACTIVITY

Review the highlights from the video session of *Marriage on the Rock* with your spouse. Look over your outline on the previous pages if needed and answer the following questions.

Fill in the blanks from Jimmy's teaching:

Danger #1 – Disregarding the Lordship of Jesus

(1) Money offers us _____ that God offers, but without any _____ _____.

(2) God's blessing on our finances not only creates _____ in our hearts, but it also releases His miracle power to _____ and _____ us.

(3) Putting God first makes Him Lord and stops _____ in marriage.

Danger #2 – Disrespecting Your Spouse's Financial Perspective

The Four Money Languages:

(1) _____ – Money means _____ whether it's a house, car or possessions. Communicates love by _____.

(2) _____ – Money means _____. Relationships are the focus. Communicates love by _____.

(3) _____ – Money means _____. Money keeps away chaos and problems. Communicates love by _____.

(4) _____ – Money means _____ and respect from desirable people. Communicates love by _____.

Danger #3 – Dominance of Money

It is common for there to be a _____ control of the money.

Whether man or woman, it is important to be _____ partners even if one spouse _____ _____ the bills.

Danger #4 – Disagreement about Financial Decisions

It is _____ to disagree and _____. The purpose of creating a _____ is that you will have a _____-_____ conversation in advance. Budgeting forces you to agree on _____ beforehand.

Danger #5 – Debt

Only consider _____ for essential items like a _____ or _____.

_____ money and live _____ your means. Save for _____.

Pay _____ for purchases. Only use credit cards if you pay them off _____.

WALK IT OUT:
COUPLE HOME DISCUSSION

Please discuss these questions with your spouse during the upcoming week. You will want to find a time that is good for both of you to talk so that you can give each other your best. This may be during a planned communication time or while on a date night.

1. What is your first reaction to the following sentence? Share your memories with your spouse.

HIM: When I think about good times we've had together without spending money, I think about...

HER: When I think about good times we've had together without spending money, I think about...

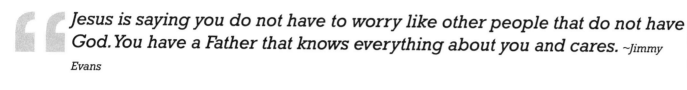

Jesus is saying you do not have to worry like other people that do not have God. You have a Father that knows everything about you and cares. ~Jimmy Evans

2. Growing up, how did your family manage money? What did you learn from them about spending, saving and giving?

HIM: My family showed me that money...

HER: My family showed me that money...

3. Who typically manages the money on a day-to-day basis in your relationship? How is this arrangement working for you and your spouse?

HIM: Lovingly, share your perspective on how the day-to-day management of the money is going...

HER: Lovingly, share your perspective on how the day-to-day management of the money is going...

4. Jimmy says that making Jesus Lord of your finances is through praying about financial decisions and also giving to your local church and those in need. Why is it sometimes a challenge to "seek God first" through praying and giving?

HIM: Praying and giving isn't always easy because...

HER: Praying and giving isn't always easy because...

5. Making the choice to give financially to church and those in need is a key way that we make Jesus Lord of our finances. Usually it is easier for one spouse to more naturally be the financial "giver" in your relationship. Who tends to give money first and how does this impact your relationship?

HIM: Who gives first, you or your wife? How does this impact your marriage?

HER: Who gives first, you or your husband? How does this impact your marriage?

> *I said, "Karen you are one of those women who are going to die with all your money in your mattress and nobody will like you." And she said, "You will not have the money to get a mattress." ~Jimmy Evans*

6. Review the money languages and their strengths and weaknesses from Jimmy's teaching. Which of the languages best describes how you view money? What do you see as the strength and weakness of your particular money language?

HIM: My money language is a(n) _____.

My financial strengths are:

My financial weaknesses are:

HER: My money language is a(n) _____.

My financial strengths are:

My financial weaknesses are:

7. Now that you've discovered your spouse's money language, what insight does that provide about how you see money, and why you sometimes disagree?

HIM: Knowing my wife's money language, helps me understand...

HER: Knowing my husband's money language, helps me understand...

8. If you have a budget, first of all, congratulate yourselves, you're already ahead. Take this time to review your budget. Does it still express your current values? As you discuss these issues, keep in mind your spouse's money language and that you both bring strengths and weaknesses to the relationship.

HIM: In general terms, concerning our spending I would like to adjust our budget by:

1.

2.

3.

HER: In general terms, concerning our spending I would like to adjust our budget by:

1.

2.

3.

> *Jesus said, "A house divided against itself falls." It is impossible to disagree and succeed. When you have chronic disagreement within a relationship it will not succeed. That is why unity is essential.* ~Jimmy Evans

If you don't have a budget, schedule a time to begin working on one. Begin by taking inventory of where your money is going and what that reflects about each of your values. After you have your list of expenses, prioritize them in order of importance. Talk about your different perspectives and as needed, how you can compromise with your spouse.

We commit to having an uninterrupted time to work on our budget on _____ at _____ o'clock.

_____

His Signature   Date

_____

Her Signature   Date

9. Gather information to determine how much debt you presently owe. What's your mortgage balance? How much do you owe on your credit cards? What loans are you paying off? Draw up a summary below so that you know exactly how much you owe and what interest rates you are paying on these debts.

	Debt	Interest	Remaining	Pay Off Date
1.				
2.				
3.				
4.				
5.				
6.				

> *Budgeting is critical not because of numbers but because of values. Budgeting is talking in advance.* ~Jimmy Evans

10. What are you and your spouse saving for on a regular basis? (If you're not saving currently, that's ok. Go on to the next question.)

1.

2.

3.

11. What would you like to be saving for, that you are currently not doing? When could you start saving for these items?

HIM: I would like us to start saving for…

1.

2.

3.

HER: I would like us to start saving for…

1.

2.

3.

"*If you are not saving money you are not living within your means.* ~*Jimmy Evans*"

Couple Prayer: *God, thank you for being our provider. We choose to seek you first and believe that you will take care of all our needs. Give us your wisdom on how to manage our money together. Thank you for our differences in how we see money. Help us financially work together and not against each other. May any resentment or tension over money dissipate and be replaced with blessing and peace in our marriage. Help us give, save and spend so that we bring honor to you and are prepared for the future. Amen.*

WRAP IT UP

Managing money can be one of the greatest blessings because it builds trust in the relationship. When we lovingly communicate our financial perspective, peace enters the financial picture.

As you agree on spending, you can have a plan to give, pay off debt and save for your goals. It takes effort and compromise to come into each other's world and realize that we make the best financial decisions together.

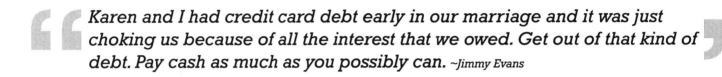

Karen and I had credit card debt early in our marriage and it was just choking us because of all the interest that we owed. Get out of that kind of debt. Pay cash as much as you possibly can. ~*Jimmy Evans*

PARENTS: PAST AND PRESENT

*Every thing we do affects
our family for generations.*

Have you ever heard the saying, "An apple doesn't fall far from the tree?" The reality is, we are more like those around us than we often want to admit.

More than any other factor in life, parents have the greatest impact on us. If your parents had a good influence on your life and then you get married, you carry that influence into your relationship.

But the problem is any negative influence that you saw from your parents, you also brought into marriage. You may not remember everything your parents said, but you do remember the example they modeled for you.

We have all been greatly influenced by our families. The good news is, we can overcome any negative behaviors in our lives so that future generations live in freedom and blessing...

DVD TEACHING WITH JIMMY EVANS

Below is an outline of today's teaching. Feel free to take additional notes in the space provided as you listen to Jimmy share biblical truths on having a successful marriage.

PARENTS: PAST AND PRESENT

Related Scriptures: Exodus 34:7, Deuteronomy 5:10, Matthew 5:33-37, James 4:13-17, Proverbs 22:15

Overcoming Iniquities

a) Everything we say and do affects our children and our grandchildren for four generations. (Exodus 34:7)

b) The Hebrew word for iniquities is "avon" which means a sin or a problem created in you because of the same issue being modeled in your parent's life.

c) Like a tree that is blown by the wind over and over, it becomes bent in the direction that it is blown. So a child is bent in the direction that he observes his parents.

d) Examples of iniquities include: anger, substance abuse, chauvinism and sexism, racism, physical abuse, verbal abuse, sexual abuse, bigotry, immorality, negativity, perfectionism, conditional love, pride, unforgiveness, gossip, etc.

e) Questions to ask yourself:

1) While growing up, were the things I was exposed to Biblically sound and morally correct?

How did your family resolve conflict?

How did your family see money?

How did your parents treat each other?

2) Do I practice the same things I didn't like about my parents?

3) Have I ever dealt properly with the things I viewed as wrong?

f) How to break family iniquities:

1) Recognize the problem. Call it what it is, a sin.

2) Take responsibility for your behavior. Don't blame your parents.

3) Forgive your parents, whether they're alive or dead.

4) Make Jesus the Lord over that area of your life.

Overcoming Inner Vows

a) An inner vow is a self-directed promise resulting from difficulty or pain. Many inner vows happen in childhood, but they can happen at any age.

b) Examples of inner vows:

"I'll never treat my children like that."

"I'll never be poor again."

"No one is ever going to hurt me again."

"I'll never _____."

"I'll always _____."

"When I grow up _____."

c) The problems with inner vows:

1) Inner vows are unscriptural. (Matthew 5:33-37)

2) When you vow something, it is not of God. (James 4:13-17)

3) Inner vows prohibit learning and growth and cause extremes.

4) Inner vows are our highest loyalty. We may resist God or others.

5) Inner vows make us a little crazy and unteachable.

d) How to break inner vows:

1) Ask God to show them to you.

2) Repent for taking that area away from God.

3) Forgive anyone who harmed you and caused you to make the vow.

4) Bring the issue to Jesus so that He can teach you.

Skills for In-Law Relations

a) Principle #1 - The Principle of Honor

1) Our parents have authority over us when we are growing up, but when we are grown their authority ends. You no longer have to obey them, but you should honor them.

2) If your parent or in-law is helping you out financially or you are living with them, they have a right to speak into your life.

3) If your parent or in-law needs help, either financially or with your time, then you need to help them.

b) Principle #2 - The Principle of Separation

1) A couple needs time together away from their parents in order to bond with each other. (Genesis 2:24)

2) When parents intrude and demand too much of a couple's time, it is unhealthy.

3) The Characteristics of a Problem In-Law

(1) Lacks bonding with their spouse.

(2) Lacks significance in their lives by pouring themselves into their children and not developing other interests.

(3) Gains excessive identity and security through their children.

(4) Becomes intrusive and even adversarial for the attention of the adult child by accusing and becoming suspicious.

4) How to handle a problem in-law:

(1) Lovingly put parameters on your time with your parents.

(2) Don't respond to manipulation or threats.

(3) Don't allow them to control your life or make your decisions.

(4) Encourage them to develop other interests and friendships. Your parents need their own friends.

c) Principle #3 – The Principle of Protection

1) If your parent becomes intrusive in your marriage, you are responsible to protect or defend your spouse.

2) Don't allow your parents to talk negatively about your spouse.

3) Don't talk badly about your spouse to your parents.

4) Don't let your parents be your marriage counselor. After you have forgiven your spouse, they will still remember.

d) Principle #4 – The Principle of Friendship

1) Treat your in-laws and parents as you would special friends.

2) If your parents cross the lines of controlling your life or not honoring your value system, speak up like you would to close friends.

3) They can't do things with your children that violate your rules. If the kids are going to be with them, parents and in-laws should be an extension of you, not a balance of you.

ADDITIONAL NOTES FROM TODAY'S TEACHING

_____

_____

_____

_____

_____

_____

_____

_____

_____

_____

_____

_____

_____

_____

_____

_____

_____

_____

TALK IT OUT:
COUPLE HOME ACTIVITY

Review the highlights from the video session of *Marriage on the Rock* with your spouse. Look over your outline on the previous pages if needed and answer the following questions.

Fill in the blanks from Jimmy's teaching:

Iniquities

Everything we say and do affects our _____ and our _____ for four _____.

How to break family iniquities:

(1) _____ the problem. Call it what it is, _____.

(2) Take _____ for your behavior. Don't _____ your parents.

(3) _____ your parents, whether they're _____ or _____.

(4) Make Jesus the _____ over that area of your life.

Inner Vows

An inner vow is a _____-_____ _____ resulting from difficulty or pain.
Many inner vows happen in _____ but they can happen at any age.

How to break inner vows:

(1) _____ God to _____ them to you.

(2) _____ for taking that area _____ from God.

(3) _____ anyone who harmed you.

(4) Bring the _____ to Jesus so He can teach you.

In-Laws

The Principle of _____ – Our parents have _____ over us when we are growing up, but when we are grown their _____ ends. You no longer have to _____ them, but you should _____ them.

The characteristics of a problem in-law:

(1) Lacks _____ with their spouse.

(2) Lacks _____ in their lives by pouring themselves into their children and not developing other interests.

(3) Gains excessive _____ and _____ through their children.

(4) Becomes _____ and even _____ for the attention of the adult child by accusing and becoming suspicious.

How to handle a problem in-law:

(1) Lovingly put _____ on your _____ with your parents.

(2) Don't respond to _____ or threats.

(3) Don't allow them to _____ your life or make your _____.

(4) Encourage them to develop other _____ and _____. Your parents need their own _____.

WALK IT OUT:
COUPLE HOME DISCUSSION

Please discuss these questions with your spouse during the upcoming week. You will want to find a time that is good for both of you to talk so that you can give each other your best. This may be during a planned communication time or while on a date night.

1. In order to understand iniquities we must consider our parents and their example we saw growing up. What experiences with your family had the biggest influence on you? (Even if your parents were absent, their absence still had an impact.) Write down the first few memories that come to mind.

HIM: From my father, I saw and learned...

1.

2.

3.

HER: From my father, I saw and learned...

1.

2.

3.

" *Karen and I both have had to break iniquities and inner vows from our past. We have wonderful parents and in-laws, but all parents are imperfect.* ~Jimmy Evans "

HIM: From my mother, I saw and learned...

1.

2.

3.

HER: From my mother, I saw and learned...

1.

2.

3.

2. The following is a list of some family iniquities. Check any trait that is strongly present in your family.

Him	Her	
☐	☐	Anger
☐	☐	Arrogance
☐	☐	Argumentativeness
☐	☐	Critical Spirit
☐	☐	Selfishness
☐	☐	Chauvinism
☐	☐	Racism
☐	☐	Perfectionism
☐	☐	Materialism
☐	☐	Sexism
☐	☐	Physical Abuse
☐	☐	Verbal Abuse
☐	☐	Substance Abuse
☐	☐	Gossip
☐	☐	Bitterness
☐	☐	Lying
☐	☐	Rebellion
☐	☐	Perfectionism
☐	☐	Unforgiveness
☐	☐	Negativity
☐	☐	Other:
☐	☐	Other:
☐	☐	Other:

An iniquity just means you grew up under a certain negative influence and you developed a bent. What they do, we tend to do. ~Jimmy Evans

3. From the list above, what undesirable behaviors or attitudes from your upbringing do you repeat as an adult?

HIM: I repeat these iniquities in my own life...

1.

2.

3.

HER: I repeat these iniquities in my own life...

1.

2.

3.

4. For the significant iniquities you identified, choose a counter-balancing blessing to pass on to your spouse and children from this point forward. (For example, if you inherited a tendency to be cold-hearted toward the suffering, you may choose to pass on a blessing of compassion.) In what practical ways can you model this "blessing" to your spouse and children?

HIM: I will change my behavior and pass on a blessing by:

1.

2.

3.

HER: I will change my behavior and pass on a blessing by:

1.

2.

3.

> " *It's a comforting thing when you're going through pain to tell yourself,* *"I'm not coming back here. No one is ever going to hurt me again."* "
> ~Jimmy Evans

5. Jimmy talked about the importance of giving your parents grace for their mistakes. Think back to how your parents were raised. How did they respond to the pain in their lives? Did they lash out, withdraw or medicate their pain? Is there a correlation between how you respond or react to issues?

HIM: My parents and I both deal with pain by...

HER: My parents and I both deal with pain by...

6. Forgiveness is an act of our will. Our feelings will follow our obedience, but the choice to forgive always comes first. Are there any areas where you need to forgive your parents? If not, then discuss a time when you've had to forgive.

HIM: I've forgiven my parents for...

1.

2.

3.

HER: I've forgiven my parents for...

1.

2.

3.

> " *When you make yourself a promise, you become God in that area. I'm taking my life over. I'm saying, "I am God of my finances and right now I'm never going to be poor again."* ~Jimmy Evans "

7. In order to help identify some inner vows, how would you answer the following question?

HIM: In the past I have thought, "I will never _____."

1.

2.

3.

In the past I have thought, "When I grow up, I will _____."

1.

2.

3.

HER: In the past I have thought, "I will never _____."

1.

2.

3.

In the past I have thought, "When I grow up, I will _____."

1.

2.

3.

8. Ask your spouse, "Are there any other iniquities or inner vows that you see in my life?" Sometimes it can be difficult to see our own issues and we need the help of someone close to us.

HIM: Here are the iniquities and inner vows my wife sees in me...

1.

2.

3.

HER: Here are the iniquities and inner vows my husband sees in me...

1.

2.

3.

> **Here's how you handle a problem in-law: you lovingly put parameters on your time with them.** *~Jimmy Evans*

9. Now let's shift gears from the parents of our past to the parents of our present.

Jimmy says that an unhealthy parent or in-law:

1. Lacks bonding with their spouse.

2. Lacks significance in other areas of their lives by pouring themselves into their children and not developing other interests.

3. Gains excessive identity and security through their children.

4. Becomes intrusive and even adversarial for the attention of the adult child by accusing and becoming suspicious.

HIM: *How have you seen these examples in the lives of your parents or in-laws?*

HER: *How have you seen these examples in the lives of your parents or in-laws?*

10. Jimmy gives the following guidelines for handling a challenging relationship with a parent or in-law:

1. Lovingly put parameters on your time with your parents.

2. Don't respond to manipulation or threats.

3. Don't allow them to control your life.

4. Encourage them to develop other interests and friendships. Your parents need their own friends.

HIM: Which of these guidelines do you need to be careful of with either your parents or your in-laws?

HER: Which of these guidelines do you need to be careful of with either your parents or your in-laws?

11. What changes do you foresee happening with your parents, in-laws and other extended family in the years to come? Discuss these issues with your spouse as you prepare for the future.

We can prepare for changes in our extended family by...

1.

2.

3.

4.

5.

12. How have your parents and in-laws been a blessing to you and your marriage? How can you love them more or create healthy boundaries where needed in the years to come?

HIM: My parents and in-laws have been a blessing by...

I can love my parents and in-laws more by...

HER: My parents and in-laws have been a blessing by...

I can love my parents and in-laws more by...

> *Do not use your parents as your marriage counselors ever. Long after you've forgotten, they'll still remember.* ~Jimmy Evans

Couple Prayer: *Father, in the name of Jesus, we confess the sin of our parents and grandparents. By the redemptive blood of Jesus Christ, we break the power of every iniquity that we have inherited and learned from our families. We also repent for the inner vows and promises we have made. Change our behavior and our thinking so that we are more like you. Today, we choose blessing for us and for future generations. We pray that you will bless our relationships with our parents, in-laws and extended family. Whether now or in the future, help us become the parents, grandparents and in-laws that honor you and bring you glory. Amen.*

WRAP IT UP

Parents have the greatest influence of showing their children what God is like and what marriage is like. More than friends, more than teachers, more than church, parents have the greatest influence.

We all want to have a positive impact on the people in our lives. As you continue to recognize and break iniquities and inner vows, you will experience amazing blessings that will continue for years to come.

Parents and in-laws can be a great blessing in your marriage if you understand the key principles that will ensure your success.

SESSION EIGHT

RAISING GREAT CHILDREN AS YOU BUILD A GREAT MARRIAGE

*How will your children succeed
if you don't show them how?*

Children are one of the greatest gifts in life. Raising children is also one of the greatest responsibilities. We are entrusted with kids for a season, but our marriage remains long after they're gone.

Children are also our greatest challenge. Parenting is a full time job that requires effort on every level: physically, emotionally, spiritually and financially.

Even though it's hard work, you can maximize the joys of raising great children as you build a great marriage...

DVD TEACHING WITH JIMMY EVANS

Below is an outline of today's teaching. Feel free to take additional notes in the space provided as you listen to Jimmy share biblical truths on having a successful marriage.

RAISING GREAT CHILDREN AS YOU BUILD A GREAT MARRIAGE

Related Scriptures: *Genesis 2:24, Mark 3:25, Proverbs 22:6*

Principle #1 – Marriage Precedes Children in Priority

a) Your marriage must be a higher priority than your children.

   1) It's damaging to believe "Nothing is important as our kids."

   2) Our relationship with God and our spouse takes priority over our children.

b) Prioritizing your marriage above your children is critical because:

   1) Marriage only works when it's most important. God's law of priority is inviolable. (Genesis 2:24) When it is violated, marriage suffers.

   2) Our relationship with God and our spouse enables us to be good parents.

   3) Your children's security and happiness comes from you having a positive relationship with God and your spouse.

   4) Raising children is a temporary task. Marriage is for a lifetime.

      You should say, "I want my child's marriage to be just like ours." If you can't say "yes" to that statement then you need to evaluate what changes need to be made.

c) Forsaking your marriage for the sake of your children will:

   1) Send you into depression when your children leave.

   2) Make you overly dependent upon your children and set you up for being a problem in-law.

   3) Make your children overly dependent upon you and set them up for future problems in their marriage.

4) Create resentment within your spouse that grows over time.

d) How to establish and protect proper priorities:

1) Establish healthy disciplines and traditions: date night, family night and couple weekends.

2) Budget your time and energy in the same manner you would your money.

3) Protect higher priorities from lower ones.

(1) Spiritual priorities must be protected. Teach the kids that God is important.

(2) Marriage priorities must be protected. Teach them that marriage is important.

Principle #2 – Unity is Essential

a) "If a house is divided against itself, that house cannot stand." - Mark 3:25, NIV

b) Four essential practices for promoting unity:

1) Always present a united front to your children.

(1) Disagree, discuss and come to a point of agreement in private.

(2) Don't make significant parenting decisions without your spouse.

2) Always honor each other in front of your children and make your children honor your spouse.

(1) Don't make your spouse defend themselves to your children.

(2) Unity means, "What happens to you is happening to me because we are a team."

3) Never allow a significant difference to develop in how you express love or enforce punishment.

(1) The danger of a "good cop-bad cop" mentality is it creates extremes where you and your spouse are opposites.

(2) Children do not develop properly if both parents are not expressing affection and enforcing discipline.

4) Go outside of your marriage for counseling and input.

(1) Nearly every couple will need to go to an outside source for counsel and wisdom because your own emotions will be too involved.

(2) Every couple should have an emergency plan for outside counsel for when they reach an impasse.

Principle #3 – Parenting Takes Faith

a) Parenting takes faith because it is a process and many of the desired results cannot be produced immediately.

b) "Train up a child in the way he should go and when he is old he will not depart from it." - Proverbs 22:6, NKJV

c) Training doesn't mean talking, it means showing them how to live successfully. Then when they face challenges, you have faith that they will return to your example one day.

d) How to exercise faith in parenting:

1) Don't blame yourself or each other for problems. Raising children is a process.

2) Don't take a picture of your circumstances and give up.

(1) Believe and confess by faith.

(2) Prophetic vs. Photographic Thinking – Prophetic thinking believes greatness is in every child because God put it there. Photographic thinking says that your child will never be better than they are right now.

3) Follow God's Word.

ADDITIONAL NOTES FROM TODAY'S TEACHING

_____

_____

_____

_____

_____

_____

TALK IT OUT:
COUPLE HOME ACTIVITY

Review the highlights from the video session of *Marriage on the Rock* with your spouse. Look over your outline on the previous pages if needed and answer the following questions.

Fill in the blanks from Jimmy's teaching:

Principle #1 – Marriage Precedes Children in Priority

Your marriage must be a higher priority than your children:

(1) It's _____ to believe "Nothing is important as our _____."

(2) Our relationship with God and our spouse takes _____ over our _____.

Prioritizing your marriage above your children is critical because:

(1) Marriage only _____ when it's most _____.

(2) Our relationship with _____ and our _____ enables us to be good parents.

(3) Your children's _____ and _____ comes from you having a positive relationship with God and your spouse.

(4) Raising children is a _____ task. Marriage is for a _____.

Principle #2 – Unity is Essential

Four essential practices for promoting unity:

(1) Always _____ a _____ front to your children.

(2) Always _____ each other in front of your children and _____ your children honor your spouse.

(3) Never allow a _____ difference to develop in how you express _____ or enforce _____.

(4) Go outside of your marriage for counseling and input.

Principle #3 – Parenting Takes Faith

Training doesn't mean _____, it means _____ them how to live successfully. Then when they face _____, you have _____ that they will return to your _____ one day.

How to exercise faith in parenting:

(1) Don't _____ yourself or each other for _____. Raising children is a _____.

(2) Don't take a _____ of your _____ and give up.

(3) Follow _____ _____.

WALK IT OUT:
COUPLE HOME DISCUSSION

Please discuss these questions with your spouse during the upcoming week. You will want to find a time that is good for both of you to talk so that you can give each other your best. This may be during a planned communication time or while on a date night.

1. What was your first reaction when hearing the principle that parents should consider their children secondary to their marriage?

HIM: When Jimmy said marriage is more important than kids, I thought...

HER: When Jimmy said marriage is more important than kids, I thought...

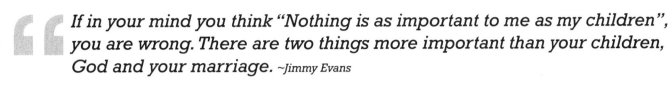

If in your mind you think "Nothing is as important to me as my children", you are wrong. There are two things more important than your children, God and your marriage. ~Jimmy Evans

2. Think about the last few weeks. Which currently ranks higher, your kids or your marriage? Discuss occasions when you might have given too much energy to the kids and not enough to your relationship

HIM: From my perspective, the kids have come before our marriage when...

HER: From my perspective, the kids have come before our marriage when...

3. Our relationship with God and our spouse creates happiness and security for our children. How have you seen this in your own family?

HIM: Our kids are happiest when...

HER: Our kids are happiest when...

HIM: When our kids see us disagree or argue, they...

HER: When our kids see us disagree or argue, they...

> **When you are struggling in your relationship, and I am talking long-term because we all have issues from time to time, your children's security comes from you being secure.** *~Jimmy Evans*

4. Do you and your spouse get enough alone time together to protect your marriage? If not, how can you arrange your schedule so that you have more time? (If you need ideas, look back on Session 2 on "The Four Foundational Laws of Marriage.") A good start is a regular communication time, a date night and a couple's weekend away from the kids.

We can make more alone time by planning...

1.

2.

3.

5. Jimmy recommends that you tell your kids, "When mom and dad go in the bedroom, don't knock on the door unless something is a real emergency." In what ways do you allow your kids too much access that it hurts your marriage? How can you set more appropriate boundaries to protect your couple time?

We can set more appropriate rules and boundaries by...

1.

2.

3.

6. When parents speak with one united voice to their children, it makes all the difference. By nature, children will try to divide their parents. When do your children try to divide you?

Our children try to divide us concerning...

1.

2.

3.

7. Reflect on your roles when it comes to parental discipline. Does one of you usually give out the punishments or do you both discipline equally? If one parent acts as the "good cop" and one as the "bad cop," it will create division and misunderstanding.

HIM: In what ways, if at all, do I comfort or discipline the kids differently than my wife?

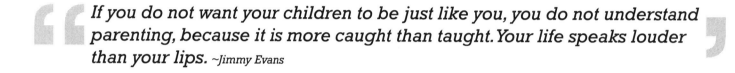

If you do not want your children to be just like you, you do not understand parenting, because it is more caught than taught. Your life speaks louder than your lips. ~Jimmy Evans

HER: In what ways, if at all, do I comfort or discipline the kids differently than my husband?

Use your discussion as a starting point for finding new ways to become more united as you discipline.

8. Why is it difficult to always present a united front to your children? How do you respond to a child when you and your spouse don't agree?

HIM: When I disagree with my wife, I tell my kids...

HER: When I disagree with my husband, I tell my kids...

9. When have you ever contradicted your spouse in front of the kids? When have you ever spoken negatively of your spouse in front of your kids? Lovingly, talk about these issues together and share your feelings with each other.

HIM: I'm sorry whenever I have not honored you in front of the children concerning...

HER: I'm sorry whenever I have not honored you in front of the children concerning...

> *What Karen and I would do is we would go in our room by ourselves and sometimes we would argue. They did not know anything about the conversation. The only thing they knew is mom and dad were a two-headed monster.* ~Jimmy Evans

10. What parenting challenges are you facing right now? For parents, a big issue is often agreeing on discipline. For children, it is common to push boundaries, and as they grow older those boundaries involve friends, clothes, television and electronics.

Begin discussing how you could become more united on these issues. (If you can't resolve a situation right now, that's ok. What's important is that you each lovingly share your perspective and get the discussion going.)

The Issue	Our United Response
1.	1.
2.	2.
3.	3.

> *When you reach an impasse, do not let it destroy your marriage. Do not let it take you out. Everyone is going to come to times in your marriage and as parents that you cannot solve the problem on your own.*
>
> ~Jimmy Evans

11. Nearly every couple at some point in their marriage will need to go to an outside source for counsel and wisdom because your own emotions will be too involved in the situation.

Whether now or in the future, where can we go for an outside perspective on parenting when we need help?

1.

2.

3.

12. Jimmy says that training doesn't mean talking, it means showing your children how to live successfully. Before the next session, ask your children, "What do you learn about marriage from us? What do you learn about conflict? What do you learn about money?" Their response may inspire you to make some further adjustments in your parenting style.

By watching us, our children said they learned that marriage...

1.

2.

3.

After talking with our children, we need to change...

1.

2.

3.

Couple Prayer: *God, we thank you so much for our children. Relating to kids helps us understand how you relate and love us. Help us prioritize our marriage first and foremost in front of our children so that we can show them how to love their future spouse. God, we repent to each other and to you for when we have not been united in front of our kids. Give us patience and faith to be the parents that you desire from this day forward. Amen*

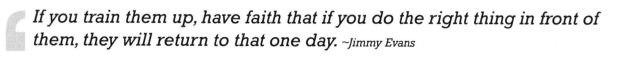

If you train them up, have faith that if you do the right thing in front of them, they will return to that one day. ~Jimmy Evans

WRAP IT UP

Three powerful principles will determine the future of your marriage and children. When you make your marriage a higher priority than your children, present a united front, and have faith during the hard times, you'll build a great marriage and raise great children.

Maintaining a marriage and raising kids is hard work, but it is possible to succeed at both simultaneously. Ultimately, a child's happiness and security is a reflection of the quality of your relationship together.

SEXUAL FULFILLMENT IN MARRIAGE

*God's design for sex
is a lifetime of pleasure and delight.*

Sex should be something we enjoy and look forward to in marriage. In a healthy relationship, there is effort and forethought given towards sex to make it fun and pleasurable.

However, Satan's ultimate goal is that we will be ashamed of our sexuality so that we won't talk about sex with our spouse. The good news is, you don't have to live a life full of frustration, shame and rejection.

Through talking about important issues, we can overcome any obstacles preventing us from experiencing sex in marriage. God's plan for sexual fulfillment works...

DVD TEACHING WITH JIMMY EVANS

Below is an outline of today's teaching. Feel free to take additional notes in the space provided as you listen to Jimmy share biblical truths on having a successful marriage.

SEXUAL FULFILLMENT IN MARRIAGE

Related Scriptures: *1 Corinthians 7:3-5*

God's Design for Sex

a) Sex is a thermometer and thermostat for your relationship.

1) A thermostat controls a certain level of happiness, intimacy and well-being. When you're having good sex, it enhances the marriage relationship. It's not everything, but it's very important.

2) A thermometer reflects the overall well-being of the marriage. If sex is bad in your marriage, you're probably not communicating and you have other issues in your marriage.

b) The number one problem that women have is the lack of desire whether physical or hormonal. The number one problem that men have is premature ejaculation.

c) God created sex for pleasure and lifelong enjoyment in marriage.

1) God is fun and He wants you to enjoy sex.

2) The devil wants us to believe that we have to go to his side to enjoy sex.

d) The parameters that God put on sex are for our protection.

1) If the Bible doesn't prohibit an intimate act, then it's up to your personal choice and consciousness.

2) Questions to ask each other: Is it consensual? Is it safe? Does it enhance the relationship?

e) God created our sexual differences to make our relationship more fulfilling.

1) Men are in tune with their emotions after sex. Women need to be emotionally in tune with their husbands to feel sexual.

2) Men are visually responsive. Women are relationally responsive.

3) Men turn on instantly. Women warm up gradually.

4) Men are emotionally modest. Women are physically modest.

5) Men are compartmental. Women are inclusive.

6) For men, orgasm is essential. For women, orgasm is optional.

7) Men desire direct sexual touching and stimulation. Women desire non-sexual affection and limited sexual touching.

The Five Ingredients to Sexual Fulfillment

a) Commit to meeting your spouse's sexual needs in a committed and faithful manner.

1) Our bodies belong to each other. We should never use our body to punish or withdraw from each other. (1 Corinthians 7:3-5)

2) We usually have different sexual needs. Twenty percent of women are more sexual than their husbands.

b) Communicate your sexual needs and allow your spouse to communicate.

1) Talk in a positive and clear way and not through negatives. ("Yes, I like this." "Try this instead.")

2) Communication should take place before, during and after sex.

c) Commit to sexual purity to protect the integrity of the marriage.

1) Don't allow fantasy or lust in your relationship. The only way to overcome temptation is to replace those thoughts with greater thoughts.

2) Don't develop inappropriate emotional or sexual relationships. Share everything in your lives, especially your phones and passwords.

3) Don't turn to sin. Give your unmet needs to God when your spouse is not meeting your needs.

4) Don't hide your temptations. Be honest and accountable. Attraction is inevitable, but you decide how to respond.

5) Don't have friends who are violating the covenant of their marriage.

d) Create an atmosphere of sexual pleasure.

1) Romance outside of the bedroom. Meet an unspoken need in your spouse that will please them. Every week have a date night.

2) Plan special sexual encounters on a regular basis at times when you have the most energy and time. Schedule sex, so that you both know what to expect. Have "his" or "her" nights.

e) Communicate and deal with sexual problems together.

1) Sexual problems affect both of you and are dangerous if not addressed in a proactive and timely manner.

2) Whether it's a lack of desire, stress, fatigue, conflict or past abuse, if you are having problems sexually your spouse is always being affected, especially if their desire for sex is greater than yours.

3) The devil knows how to speak both of our languages related to temptation.

(1) For men it's pornography. The deception is that women are less emotional and just sexual.

(2) For women it's romance novels and soap operas. The deception is that men are less sexual and just emotional.

(3) The best way to succeed is not try to change the unchangeable. Accepting your spouse for who they are. If you try to make them into somebody not real, you're going to fail.

ADDITIONAL NOTES FROM TODAY'S TEACHING

_____

_____

_____

_____

_____

_____

_____

_____

TALK IT OUT:
COUPLE HOME ACTIVITY

Review the highlights from the video session of *Marriage on the Rock* with your spouse. Look over your outline on the previous pages if needed and answer the following questions.

Fill in the blanks from Jimmy's teaching:

God's Design for Sex

God created sex for _____ and _____ _____ in marriage.

The parameters that God put on sex are for our _____.

(1) If the Bible doesn't _____ an intimate act, then it's up to your _____ _____ and consciousness.

(2) Questions to ask each other: Is it _____? Is it _____? Does it _____ the relationship?

Our Sexual Differences

(1) Men are in tune with their _____ after sex. Women need to be emotionally in tune with their _____ to feel sexual.

(2) Men are _____ responsive. Women are _____ responsive.

(3) Men turn on _____. Women warm up _____.

(4) Men are _____ modest. Women are _____ modest.

(5) Men are _____. Women are _____.

(6) For men, orgasm is _____. For women, orgasm is _____.

(7) Men desire _____ sexual _____ and stimulation. Women desire non-sexual _____ and _____ sexual touching.

The Five Ingredients to Sexual Fulfillment

(1) Commit to _____ your spouse's sexual needs in a _____ and faithful manner.

(2) _____ your sexual needs and _____ your spouse to communicate.

(3) Commit to _____ _____ to protect the integrity of the marriage.

(4) Create an _____ of sexual _____.

(5) _____ and deal with sexual _____ together.

WALK IT OUT:
COUPLE HOME DISCUSSION

Please discuss these questions with your spouse during the upcoming week. You will want to find a time that is good for both of you to talk so that you can give each other your best. This may be during a planned communication time or while on a date night.

1. Knowing that you and your spouse will have different desires at different times, answer the following question together.

HIM: For me, I would like to have sex:

a) More often

b) Less often

c) At our current pace

HER: For me, I would like to have sex:

a) More often

b) Less often

c) At our current pace

God wants you to enjoy sex in marriage and to have that enjoyment for the rest of your married life. It's very, very important.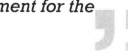
~Jimmy Evans

2. What do you think of God's plan for sex in marriage? Have you ever believed that the Christian life limits your fun in sex? Do you still feel this way?

HIM: I think God's plan for sex is...

HER: I think God's plan for sex is...

3. When one of you doesn't want to have sex, how do you respond to each other? What would you like to hear from your spouse when they're not in the mood?

HIM: When my wife doesn't want to have sex, she...

HER: When my husband doesn't want to have sex, he...

HIM: When my wife doesn't want to have sex, I would like to hear...

HER: When my husband doesn't want to have sex, I would like to hear...

4. How do the differences between you and your spouse impact your sex life? How are your differences positive for your relationship?

HIM: Our differences impact us by...

HER: Our differences impact us by...

> **So you're asking, "What can we do in sex in marriage?" A bunch! You can do a whole lot. You should have a big time having sex in marriage.** *~Jimmy Evans*

5. Review the notes on "The Five Ingredients to Sexual Fulfillment."

(1) Commit to meeting your spouse's sexual needs in a committed and faithful manner.

(2) Communicate your sexual needs and allow your spouse to communicate.

(3) Commit to sexual purity to protect the integrity of the marriage.

(4) Create an atmosphere of sexual pleasure.

(5) Communicate and deal with sexual problems together.

Choose one of the five ingredients of sexual fulfillment to work on in your relationship.

HIM: For my wife, I can work on...

HER: For my husband, I can work on...

6. Remembering that sex is God's subject, ask your spouse, "What do I do to you before, during or after sex that you really like?"

HIM: I really like it when you...

1.

2.

3.

HER: I really like it when you...

1.

2.

3.

> *About 20% of women are more sexual than their husbands, but it doesn't matter who is more sexual. The only thing that matters is that you say to your spouse, "I'm committed to meeting your sexual needs."* ~*Jimmy Evans*

7. God made sex to be fun and exciting. Is there anything that you would like to try sexually? Talk about this with your spouse. (Remember the three questions: Is it consensual? Is it safe? Does it enhance the relationship?)

HIM: I would really like to try...

HER: I would really like to try...

8. We need to be willing to talk openly about our sexual problems together, especially as we grow

older and our desires change. Most everyone is going to experience sexual challenges at some point in their marriage. When this happens what will you do? (If you and your spouse have already dealt with this, then talk about the issue with each other.)

HIM: When I have a sexual problem I will...

HER: When I have a sexual problem I will...

> *We talked about the things I like and don't like. We talked about the things she likes and dislikes. It was the greatest discussion we ever had and it changed our sex life.* ~Jimmy Evans

9. Jimmy recommends scheduling sex on a regular basis. When can you and your spouse plan to have sexual encounters? Even if this seems non-spontaneous it actually builds excitement and gives you both something to look forward to together.

We plan on "being together" regularly on _____ at _____ o'clock.

_____

His Signature   Date

_____

Her Signature   Date

10. Jimmy talked about creating an atmosphere of sexual pleasure in your marriage. (It doesn't just happen, you have to make it happen!)

HIM: For me, a "his night" would include...

1.

2.

3.

HER: For me, a "her night" would include...

1.

2.

3.

Now make plans for an upcoming very special evening together. Maybe plan a romantic night out on the town: dinner, dancing, whatever you like. Then extend the romance with a night of sexual fun at home or at a hotel room. Here's the key: pick a date in the near future to actually carry out your plan for your very special night.

We plan on having a "very special night" on _____ at _____ o'clock. I'll plan and prepare to give my best to you.

_____   _____
His Signature   Date

_____   _____
Her Signature   Date

The only way you can overcome sexual temptation is to take control of your thoughts. You can't take thoughts out of your mind. You can only replace them with greater thoughts. ~Jimmy Evans

Couple Prayer: *God, we thank you that you created sex and that you made sex wonderful. We want to have a sex life that honors our marriage and honors you. Help us continue to talk about our sexual needs and desires with each other. Give us understanding when our spouse's needs are different than our own. Create sexual purity in our lives so that we will not reject each other, but lovingly serve one another. We don't want our passion to diminish with age, but rather we want to experience intimacy for the rest of our lives. Amen.*

WRAP IT UP

Sex is special and a gift from God that is sacred to marriage. We are different by God's design and when we respect and serve each other sexually, we complete each other and our marriage becomes fulfilling for both of us.

We have to work at creating a pure sexual atmosphere in our marriage where we can communicate, pursue each other and meet each others needs. We have to be committed to working out problems promptly when they arise and as our sexual needs change throughout life.

It's especially important to women that you romance your wife and meet her emotional needs. Pursue her and have a date night where you take care of her emotional needs.

FOUNDATIONS FOR SUCCESSFUL BLENDED FAMILIES

Marriage is permanent.
Parenting is temporary.

The past is an issue in all of our lives that affects our marriages and families. However, blended families have special dynamics that often immediately set up serious challenges.

Blended families are defined as a marriage where one or both spouses bring children with them from a previous marriage or relationship. And no matter how "blended" the families are, there are always additional complexities.

Even though blended families have special challenges, they also have special joys...

DVD TEACHING WITH JIMMY EVANS

Below is an outline of today's teaching. Feel free to take additional notes in the space provided as you listen to Jimmy share biblical truths on having a successful marriage.

FOUNDATIONS FOR SUCCESSFUL BLENDED FAMILIES

Related Scriptures: *Ephesians 4:30-32, Genesis 2:24-25, Proverbs 22:6*

Dynamic #1 - Unresolved Feelings for a Prior Relationship

a) Ten years after divorce 50% of people still have feelings of love for their ex-spouse. Marriage (and sexual intimacy) joins our soul together with another person.

b) Satan either perverts our memories or poisons them to ruin our future.

   1) When we're married, Satan is the accuser of our spouse.

   2) When we divorce, he reminds us of what was right.

   3) Thank God for any good in the prior relationship. Then decide, "I leave it behind and I'm focused on the person I'm with right now."

   4) We must forgive. It doesn't make the person who hurts us right, but it makes us free.

Dynamic #2 - Lower Trust and Higher Expectations

a) Lower Trust: "I have less good will and am more suspicious of your motives and actions. I'm not getting my heart broken again."

b) Higher Expectations: "I expect more of you because of my previous disappointments. I expect you will not make the same mistakes my ex made."

c) How to establish trust in your current relationship:

   1) Before and after marriage, date to establish trust.

   2) Disassociate the past from the present. Forgive and go on.

   3) Dream new dreams. Set goals for your marriage. Have an annual vision retreat.

Dynamic #3 – Inner Vows

a) An inner vow is a self-promise when we are going through difficulty to comfort ourselves. "No one will ever hurt me like this again."

b) Inner vows are sinful because they deny God authority over our lives. Inner vows cause us to overreact to life's situations.

c) How to break inner vows:

  1) Recognize when you were hurt and what happened.

  2) Renounce and forgive the person who has hurt you.

  3) Request God's guidance and give Him control.

Dynamic #4 - Non-Biological Parenting

a) If you are the biological parent, don't let your protective instincts keep your child away from the step-parent.

  1) The biological parent should enforce discipline, but both parents have authority and stand as a united front.

  2) The non-biological parent should always honor the child's parent and never try to replace them.

  3) You should trust each other with decisions related to the children or stepchildren. There is no place for favoritism or the attitude, "You don't love them like I love them."

b) Natural sexual barriers may be missing. Wear appropriate clothing around non-biological children, especially teenagers and young adults.

c) Child support needs to be paid with a good attitude. (Remember the Law of Possession, marriage is sharing. "Your debts are my debts.")

d) Visitation can be a source of conflict and stress.

  1) Let the adults communicate and don't use the children as messengers.

  2) Every time the children leave your home. Pray over the children that God will protect their minds, hearts and sexuality.

  3) Thank God for every day that you have with them. Be fun and fair, but have righteous standards in your home.

4) Have faith and trust God to do what you can't. (Proverbs 22:6)

The Priority of Marriage

a) Marriage is the nucleus of the family. You can't build a marriage around children, but you can build children around a marriage.

b) Marriage is permanent. Parenting is a temporary assignment.

1) How will your children succeed in marriage if you don't show them how?

2) If your children's hurts were caused by a broken marriage, they can be cured by a good one.

3) When they leave, you will have a stable life and they won't be emotionally needy.

c) Remember the Four Foundational Laws of Marriage:

1) The Law of Priority – Your marriage is the relationship you focus on now. Love your children and give them quality time, but marriage comes first.

2) The Law of Pursuit – Make dating your spouse a priority, especially when you've had a shorter newlywed season in a blended family

3) The Law of Possession – The non-biological parent has to be an equal in the relationship. Equality among the kids is especially important in a blended family.

4) The Law of Purity – Take responsibility for your mistakes. Use the pain of your past and create a great future for your family.

ADDITIONAL NOTES FROM TODAY'S TEACHING

_____

_____

_____

_____

_____

TALK IT OUT:
COUPLE HOME ACTIVITY

Review the highlights from the video session of *Marriage on the Rock* with your spouse. Look over your outline on the previous pages if needed and answer the following questions.

Fill in the blanks from Jimmy's teaching:

Dynamic #1 – Unresolved Feelings

Ten years after divorce _____% of people still have feelings of _____ for their ex-spouse

Satan either _____ our memories or _____ them to ruin our future.

Thank God for any _____ in the _____ relationship. Then decide, "I _____ it behind and I'm _____ on the person I'm with right now."

Dynamic #2 – Lower Trust and Higher Expectations

How to establish trust in your current relationship:

(1) Before and after marriage, _____ to establish trust.

(2) _____ the past from the present. _____ and go on.

(3) Dream new _____. Set _____ for your marriage. Have an annual _____ _____.

Dynamic #3 – Inner Vows

Inner vows are _____ because they _____ God authority over our lives. Inner vows cause us to _____ to life's situations.

Dynamic #4 – Non-Biological Parenting

The _____ parent should _____ discipline, but both parents have _____ and stand as a united front.

The non-biological parent should always _____ the child's _____ and never try to _____ them.

You should _____ each other with decisions related to the children or stepchildren. There is no place for _____ or the attitude, "You don't love them like I love them."

The Priority of Marriage

Marriage is _____. Parenting is a _____ assignment.

How will your children _____ in marriage if you don't _____ them how?

If your children's _____ were caused by a _____ marriage, they can be _____ by a good one.

When they leave, you will have a _____ life and they won't be emotionally _____.

WALK IT OUT:
COUPLE HOME DISCUSSION

Please discuss these questions with your spouse during the upcoming week. You will want to find a time that is good for both of you to talk so that you can give each other your best. This may be during a planned communication time or while on a date night.

A lot of people in blended families feel like they did something wrong or they kind of feel guilty. Are you not glad that God loves us all the same?

1. Ten years after divorce, Jimmy says that 50% of ex-spouses still have feelings for the person in the previous relationship.

HIM: From your perspective, when have you seen this to be true?

HER: From your perspective, when have you seen this to be true?

2. Whether it was a previous marriage or relationship, talk with your spouse about your feelings of the past. Bring it into the light, so that you both can have a fresh start. Without realizing it, often we have our guard up concerning our past hurts that we bring into marriage.

HIM: I've been hurt by relationships when...

1.

2.

3.

HER: I've been hurt by relationships when...

1.

2.

3.

3. Make a decision together that each of your past relationships are just that, they are past history. Appreciate the good in your past, but focus on the present with your spouse and family.

HIM: Why is it so important for a married couple to live in the present?

HER: Why is it so important for a married couple to live in the present?

> " *Just thank God for any good that was in that relationship and put it in the past. When the devil comes to you in bad times and he brings back memories from the past, stop it.* ~Jimmy Evans "

4. Jimmy says that you need to set goals together for your marriage. What are some goals that you would like to accomplish together in the future? If they are family goals, discuss how your children could become part of the process as well.

Our goals for the next 5, 10 or 20 years are...

1.

2.

3.

4.

5.

5. We naturally come into a blended marriage suspicious of a person's motives and actions. We don't want to get our hearts broken again while expecting improvement over our past failures. Consequently, we have to re-establish trust and expectations of our current marriage.

HIM: What do you need from your wife in order to trust her?

HER: What do you need from your husband in order to trust him?

> *Marriage is trust. When I marry you what I am saying is, "I am entrusting my life to you. I am entrusting everything I have including the most precious thing, my children, to you."* ~Jimmy Evans

6. Discuss the role of a step-parent. How does society view step-parents? What do you believe is God's perspective?

HIM: What are some healthy and unhealthy step-parents you've seen?

HER: What are some healthy and unhealthy step-parents you've seen?

7. Discuss how you and your spouse currently handle discipline and your relationships with the children. Remember, what's most important is that even though you are a blended family that you both present a united front to the kids.

Concerning discipline, what is working and where is improvement needed?

Many times children undermine the new marriage because they see it as an end of the hope of their parents getting back together. Even though you and you spouse fell in love, it can take many years for children in a blended family to feel like they fit in. (Think of a blended family as a crock pot, it takes a lot of time.) Remember, you may have moved on from your previous relationship but a child will have a relationship with the biological parent for the rest of their life.

8. It can be difficult to understand that marriage must come first in a blended family. Biological parents tend to be over protective because they do not want their children to be hurt again.

HIM: From your perspective, if the children are first, why will the blended family inevitably struggle?

HER: From your perspective, if the children are first, why will the blended family inevitably struggle?

> *Your emotions may be actually working against you because of what you have been through. The objectivity of the non-biological parent may be the best gift that God has ever given you.* ~Jimmy Evans

9. Discuss what you are teaching your kids about marriage. Brainstorm ideas together of how you can better show them that marriage is a priority in your relationship.

We are teaching our kids that marriage is...

1.

2.

3.

Going forward as a family, we want our kids to see that marriage is...

1.

2.

3.

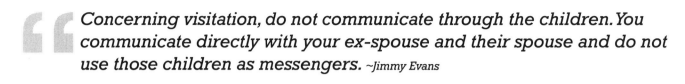

Concerning visitation, do not communicate through the children. You communicate directly with your ex-spouse and their spouse and do not use those children as messengers. ~Jimmy Evans

10. As a blended family, what did this session confirm that you are doing right in your relationship?

Jimmy confirmed that we are doing right...

1.

2.

3.

11. Where is improvement needed to have a more successful blended family?

In our blended family, we need to work on...

1.

2.

3.

Couple Prayer: *God, we thank you that every family can succeed. You have brought our family together. You are a God of restoration and you can make all things new. We decide that our past is in the past and we trust that you have a great future for our family. Help us lovingly discipline our children and stepchildren in a way that honors you and each other. Above all, we commit to making our marriage first and to provide a positive example of a successful marriage for generations. Amen.*

Marriage is the nucleus of the family, not the children. Children are a temporary assignment. They will not be there for a long time. And when they leave, they do not want you following them around. ~*Jimmy Evans*

WRAP IT UP

Blended families have special challenges, but they also have special joys. Whether it's your marriage relationship or the challenge of raising children, together commit to dealing with any issues that you may be facing. Have faith and trust God to do what you cannot.

Most marriages start with the relationship, and then children arrive later. In a blended family, children are present when the relationship begins. Marriage must come first in importance. It is of higher significance than the children. Children are a wonderful temporary assignment, but marriage is for life.